One kiss
was all he asked

...yet his gray eyes were devouring her with a hunger that made her knees weak. It would be absurd to refuse one kiss. It was impossible to say no. She raised her face.

His voice was husky. "You'll never know how many times I've wanted you in my arms."

"Clint," she whispered, then was silent as he turned. With disarming lightness his lips grazed hers, then her cheek, before returning again to her mouth in a tantalizing, feathery touch that changed to a probing, velvety warmth that was impossible to resist.

The wind, the swirling, cold flakes of snow diminished to nothing next to the storm of his kiss...

Dear Reader:

We've had thousands of wonderful surprises at SECOND CHANCE AT LOVE since we launched the line in June 1981.

We knew we were going to have to work hard to bring you the six best romances we could each month. We knew we were working with a talented, caring group of authors. But we *didn't* know we were going to receive such a warm and generous response from readers. So the thousands of wonderful surprises are in the form of letters from readers like you who've been kind with your praise, constructive and helpful with your suggestions. We read each letter...and take it seriously.

It's been a thrill to "meet" our readers, to discover that the people who read SECOND CHANCE AT LOVE novels and write to us about them are so remarkable. Our romances can only get better and better as we learn more and more about you, the reader, and what you like to read.

So, I hope you will continue to enjoy SECOND CHANCE AT LOVE and, if you haven't written to us before, please feel free to do so. If you have written, keep in touch.

With every good wish,

Sincerely,

Carolyn Nichols

Carolyn Nichols
SECOND CHANCE AT LOVE
The Berkley/Jove Publishing Group
200 Madison Avenue
New York, New York 10016

P.S. Because your opinions *are* so important to us, I urge you to fill out and return the questionnaire in the back of this book.

Second Chance at Love

RECKLESS LONGING
DAISY LOGAN

A
SECOND CHANCE AT LOVE
BOOK

Second Chance at Love books are published by
The Berkley/Jove Publishing Group
200 Madison Avenue, New York, NY 10016

To Florence, with gratitude

chapter 1

RAIN BEAT AGAINST windows of the public relations office of the Oklahoma State Conservation Department. In the silence of her small office, Lisa Callaway opened the top drawer of her desk and withdrew the letter to read it once more. Her blue eyes clouded. Clint was coming home. Why had he written to her? The bold scrawl on thick, cream-colored paper stirred her memory of gray eyes, black hair, and Clint's tall, trim frame.

With determination she stuffed the letter into the envelope and shoved it into the drawer. That part of her life was over. She could think of Clint calmly, without emotion. Thank heavens for it, too! Her only regret was that she had not gone ahead with the divorce. A sigh escaped her full, rosy lips as she smoothed a strand of golden hair into her chignon.

Her thoughts were interrupted when Eileen Weston entered the office. Eileen's sensual lips curved eagerly. "How was the interview?" she asked.

"Fine." Lisa rose to cross to a filing cabinet. "We're going out to dinner to continue it," she replied. She heard Eileen's sharp intake of breath and turned. Did Eileen think she and Tom were getting involved? Lisa's blue eyes studied Eileen. "We'll merely finish the interview we started today."

Eileen laughed. "Don't worry. Tom Perkins and I are old friends." Eileen tilted her head to one side. "Lisa, you said you and your husband are separated, that he lives in Peru."

Smoothing the sleeves of a navy sweater, which matched her woolen skirt, Lisa returned to her desk. "That's right." She sat down and crossed long, shapely legs. "He runs a branch of his father's company."

Eileen's green eyes sparkled with interest. "Oh ho! You didn't tell me his father had his own company. What's the name of it?"

A feeling of dread welled up in Lisa. She spoke softly. "Callaway and—"

"Callaway and Associates?" Eileen interrupted. She shook her red curls vigorously. "Lisa, you can't mean it! The consulting engineers for highway construction?"

Bleakly, Lisa nodded.

"But they're the firm you're opposing in your campaign to prevent construction of a road around the lake. Does Mr. Spradling know that?"

Lisa nodded. "The boss knows, Eileen."

"You said you're getting a divorce." Eileen studied her with speculation. "Does your husband plan to return from Peru?"

"Yes, he'll be home soon, as a matter of fact," Lisa replied quietly.

Eileen's eyes narrowed. "Are you certain you want a divorce?"

Lisa nodded grimly.

"How do you know you won't be able to work things out when he returns?"

As if forgetting Eileen's presence, Lisa spoke her thoughts aloud. "I've changed while he's been gone; I've made it on my own here. I haven't accepted so much as a dollar from either Clint or his family."

"Lisa, would you like some free advice?"

Lisa smiled ruefully, in the knowledge that no matter what she replied, she would receive the frank suggestion. Her slender fingers opened a drawer to remove a ledger.

Eileen spoke. "Maybe you're too independent, Lisa. You never loosen up around men. You have too good a figure to hide in this dry old office. I'd put up with a lot if I had a husband who owned a successful business." She shrugged one shoulder, causing the clinging jersey to pull taut over a voluptuous figure. "I should talk, with two marriages in my past." Eileen glanced at her watch. "It's quitting time. You're not going to start on something now, are you?"

"I may work for a short time."

Eileen shivered and rubbed her arms. "Not me. I don't let the sun set on me in this office. It's creepy here when everyone is gone. We need a security guard in that parking lot. Won't you be late for your dinner with Tom?"

Lisa shook her head. "I'm not staying long."

Eileen shrugged and turned away. "'Night, Lisa. Have a good time."

Lisa called, "Eileen, are you certain it's all right . . . for me to go out with Tom Perkins?"

Eileen grinned over her shoulder. "Sure. We're old friends. Anyway, anything goes, where men are concerned. It's every woman for herself." She waved and disappeared from view.

Lisa smiled and bent over the ledger. Within moments she was absorbed in her work and was unaware of people moving to and fro in the hall outside her office. Quiet settled over the building until it was broken by the renewed drumming of rain against the windows.

Finally Lisa closed the ledger, put things away, then donned a raincoat and headed for the door. Turning out lights as she went, she stepped into the rain and clutched the collar of her raincoat tightly around her neck. The small lot, enclosed on all sides by brick walls and cedars, except for the driveways, held only her yellow car. The icy January rain had changed to a fine sleet that stung her cheeks.

Just as she stepped away from the door, a car roared

around the corner of the building. Lisa jumped back out of its path. The sleek sports car swerved, sending a spray of water over her legs.

Angrily, Lisa glared after the car. No doubt the man had cut through the private drive to avoid the stoplight on the corner. She hurried across the lot, then noticed with dismay that the car had braked and was backing toward her.

Sudden awareness of her vulnerability swept over her. The parking lot was secluded, the building empty, and she was totally alone, except for the driver of the car.

Catching her breath, Lisa rushed ahead. Every fiber of her being was alert; her ears were attuned to each sound. The car whipped around in a semicircle and slowed into a place beside her.

Lisa fumbled for her keys. Her purse dropped to the paving, and its contents spilled out. A car door slammed, and a male voice said, "Hello."

Wildly she jammed the key into the lock.

"Hey!" he called.

She glanced over her shoulder to see a large man headed toward her. She scooped up what she could of her purse and its contents. Her compact rolled under the car, but she ignored it. With a quickening heartbeat she slid onto the seat. But before she could shut the door, strong fingers closed in an iron grip around her arm.

"Let go of me!" Lisa cried, attempting to pull free.

The man leaned down. His face was hidden in the shadows of a furry parka. Fright enveloped her, and a scream began to rise in her throat.

"Lisa!"

Shocked, she froze and gazed up at him. She faced a stranger, a man she did not recognize, but she knew the voice. Clint. No one else she knew had that husky edge to his tone.

In tiny staccatos, sleet drummed against the car, and

time halted while she peered in wonder at the man leaning over her.

"Move over so I can get in," he commanded.

Numbly, she did as he instructed. She shifted away from him until she was pressed tightly against the opposite door. She watched him sit beside her. He filled the car. His shoulders were far broader than she remembered. The hand that reached to close the door was deeply tanned.

With a shake of his head the parka dropped to his shoulders, and he turned to face her. For a long, electrifying moment they assessed each other.

Lisa couldn't believe what she saw. No one could change so much in little over a year; yet he had. His boyish thinness was gone. The lean, harsh lines of his face had changed, matured. He looked older than twenty-nine.

His features were too rugged to be called handsome, and they had become more so in the intervening time. A scar, which had not been there before, ran along his jaw.

His nose was crooked—another change. The powerful shoulders were not hidden, but accentuated, by the parka.

Lisa could not shake off the feeling of facing a caged tiger, a wild, primitive power held unpredictably in check.

She glanced down at his strong, blunt fingers, then looked up as she remembered too clearly the pleasures they could evoke. Sharply, she pulled her thoughts away from traitorous memories. In that lay destruction of the peace of mind she had achieved over the past months.

"You've changed," she whispered.

"You haven't," he answered. "You're as beautiful as ever. I'm sorry if I gave you a fright."

A degree of normalcy was returning to Lisa, and with

it, a growing sense of anger. Clint's arrogance had not changed. How typical of him to suddenly appear and expect her to be at his beck and call.

She wriggled with impatience. "Clint, there is nothing for us to say to each other...."

His steady, impassive gaze was unsettling. "That's not much of a welcome home, Lisa," he stated quietly.

She took a deep breath. "It was not intended to be. I should have gotten the divorce while you were away, but I didn't. I'll call an attorney tomorrow."

His eyes narrowed. "Will you have dinner with me tonight?"

She shook her head, suddenly thankful for Tom Perkins. "I have a date, and if I don't go soon, I'll be late for it."

The gray eyes changed to ice. "Who is he?"

Why was her heart pounding? She answered calmly enough. "That's none of your business, Clint. Now, if you don't mind, would you please get out?"

"Get out of your life, you mean," he growled.

"You were happy enough to do that before," she rejoined.

He sighed. "Will you have dinner with me tomorrow night? I want to talk to you."

"Clint—"

"Lisa," he interrupted, "you're causing our company a great deal of difficulty. The least you can do is sit down and discuss it with me."

So that was why he'd come. She nodded. "Very well, Clint, but I don't hope for much understanding."

Suddenly his mouth curved in the old, familiar lopsided grin. "You have no intention of changing your stand."

It was impossible to keep the edge out of her voice. "Clint..."

"Relax, honey," he remarked.

Honey. What memories that stirred. She closed her

eyes in desperation. All the things she thought she had forgotten, the hurts she had overcome, threatened to start tumbling down on her. "What time tomorrow, Clint?" she asked.

His gray eyes were intense, penetrating, and she looked down at her hands to avoid his direct study.

"About seven," he answered. After opening the door of the car, he regarded her in silence a moment before he murmured, "I'll see you tomorrow night, Lisa."

He stepped out, knelt, and retrieved all the items she had dropped. She scooted over to the driver's side, then accepted her belongings from his outstretched hands. His warm fingers brushed hers. Lisa inhaled sharply at the tingling awareness that coursed through her. She met his gaze and felt an exasperating warmth flood her cheeks.

"Lisa—" he began, but she spoke quickly.

"Clint, I don't want to keep Tom waiting."

His features hardened, and he stepped back. He glanced around. "Are you always the last to leave?"

She shook her head. "Occasionally. You just startled me."

"This is a secluded spot. If you needed help, you wouldn't get any."

"Clint, that's my problem," she stated, and gained another inscrutable stare. "I'll see you tomorrow night."

She closed the door and started the motor. When she turned the car to leave, he was already pulling away in the opposite direction. Unable to resist, Lisa continued to glance in the rearview mirror until the low-slung black car was out of sight.

chapter 2

SUDDENLY SHE FELT DRAINED. All this time she had thought she was completely over Clint. She had been certain she could face him without any stirring of emotion. A sob threatened to rise in her throat. She had spent less than a quarter of an hour with him, and every nerve felt raw. She shook her head resolutely. Perhaps that was natural, since he had caught her by surprise. Maybe each time, now, she could view him with more equanimity.

It wasn't until she stepped out of her car that Lisa realized Clint hadn't asked for her address. She wasn't listed in the directory. For an instant she frowned, then with a slight shrug she got out of the car.

When she unlocked and opened her apartment door, Lisa halted in mild shock. She had forgotten the state of her apartment. Sheet-covered furniture, dropcloths, buckets of paint, brushes, and newspapers were strewn around the room.

Tomorrow night Clint would arrive to pick her up for their date. She bit her lip and frowned. It shouldn't matter at all, but it did. Pride made her want him to see how established and self-sufficient she had become. Glancing at her watch, she realized there was no time to do anything except get ready for her date. Reluctantly, she headed toward the shower.

Dinner with Tom proved to be a pleasant interlude. His blond hair gleamed dully in the candlelight. While they waited for lobster dinners, he produced a pad.

"Business first—we'll get it out of the way. Let me check my facts; we didn't have very long this afternoon." He glanced down, then looked at her. "You said the city hired an agency to produce a plan for long-range development. Residential areas are increasing rapidly to the northeast, and we'll need a major highway to carry the heavy flow of traffic. The agency suggested a freeway around Lake Dodson. Their choices were through a quiet, exclusive residential area, or around the lake. The transportation commission selected the lake site. Now you've asked the commissioners and the City Council for a new hearing, and they've granted your request."

He glanced at her, and Lisa nodded. "That's correct."

From under heavy blond brows, his dark eyes regarded her carefully. "You're stirring up quite a fuss, you know."

She felt her cheeks grow warm. "I suppose I am. At least I'm on the side of my office."

"How did you get into this?"

She smoothed the linen tablecloth while she talked. "When these projects come up, our department runs routine checks on various conservation aspects. The more I began to read about the lake and its environment, the more opposed to this highway I became."

"Why?"

"I went into some of that this afternoon. The lake is home for many migratory birds, which would be driven away by the noise and pollution of the highway. It would be harmful not only to the migratory birds, but also to the permanent residents—chickadees, swallows, wrens, goldfinches, yellow-headed blackbirds. Many species that flock to the lake would be disturbed."

He shifted and studied her. "Now the question I didn't have time for when we talked earlier. Don't you have a personal stake in all this?"

"Not really," she replied stiffly.

He smiled. "No offense intended," he stated in a gentle tone.

"I'm sorry," she apologized. "I didn't mean to sound angry."

He waved his hand. "That's all right. If my figures are correct, there have been three engineering firms bidding on this project, right?"

"Yes."

He glanced at his notes. "Jones and Henderson, North Engineering, Incorporated"—he raised his head, and his dark eyes bore into hers—"and Callaway and Associates." She nodded and waited, while he asked, "Are you related to Callaway and Associates?"

She laughed easily. "I think you knew the answer to that before you asked. Yes."

His widening grin confirmed her suspicions. "I did," he admitted. "So you're opposing your husband's firm in this construction. I understand they won the bid."

Choosing her words with care, she replied, "The second half of your statement is correct. As to the first—opposing my husband's firm—I'd have to say, not exactly."

Tom Perkins waited quietly. Lisa struggled to find the best words. "My husband is in charge of a branch of Callaway in Peru. He hasn't been personally involved in this office, since he's been out of the country for more than a year...."

He interrupted her to ask quietly, "You mean you haven't seen your husband in over a year?"

"He's back now." Lisa hated the warmth she felt in her cheeks. She was thankful her voice sounded strong and indifferent.

"The man must be a total fool!" Tom Perkins said with such feeling that her embarrassment evaporated instantly. Lisa laughed at the heated tone of his voice.

He spoke quickly. "I mean it." In a swift movement

he leaned forward and reached across the table to catch her hand in his. "Eileen told me you were separated, but that's all she said."

The waiter interrupted their discussion to pour glasses of chablis, then place bowls of crisp salad before them. While they ate, Tom said, "The pictures I took today turned out well."

"You had them developed?"

"Yes. I'll show them to you next time I see you."

He ate a bite of salad, then looked at her. "I hear you're going to receive an award for your conservation efforts."

"That's right," she replied. "It has nothing to do with Lake Dodson. It's for articles I wrote last year and a campaign our Department ran."

"I'd like to write that up. Pictures too."

She smiled. "If you'd like, I'd be happy if you'd go to the awards banquet with me."

"I'd be delighted to," he answered quickly.

"It's not until next month."

He smiled. "Fine. By then I should know a lot more about you."

Suddenly Lisa thought of Clint. Perhaps she shouldn't have asked Tom Perkins to attend the banquet with her. She shrugged away the idea as ridiculous. By then divorce proceedings most likely would be under way.

Tom raised his glass of chablis in a toast. "Here's to a successful campaign to stop the road around Lake Dodson."

Lisa raised her glass and drank silently. Tom regarded her with a smile. "This is just the kind of news story I've been waiting for."

A twinge of wariness struck Lisa. Suddenly it worried her that this objective reporter had so quickly become an advocate of her project. "Maybe I've started something I'll regret."

"Indeed not! I'd like some pictures of you at the lake. Next week when the weather has cleared, will you go out there with me?"

She nodded but gazed at him thoughtfully while a feeling of gloom settled over her.

The next morning, pressing problems in the office forced her to set aside her intention to call an attorney. By the time she finally did phone, the lawyer was gone for the week.

Leaving work two hours early, Lisa returned home to do her best to make the apartment presentable. Finally she paused and studied the results. With satisfaction she regarded the gleaming polished floor surrounding lime-and-white accent rugs. Adding to the lightness were yellow-cushioned chairs and a sofa.

She'd arranged plants beside the bay window and hung pictures on the walls. Contrasting strangely with three walls of fresh white, one wall remained to be painted. In spite of it, the room was cheerful and bright. Wiping her hands on her jeans, Lisa picked up the last bucket and placed it in the broom closet.

She showered, dried her hair, then studied her clothes. After a few minutes' deliberation, she chose a white wool dress with a cowl neck and long, tapered sleeves. While she vigorously brushed her gleaming gold hair away from her face and caught it in a clip behind her neck, she mentally rehearsed what she wanted to tell Clint. She would explain her position about the lake, inform him that she intended to get the divorce right away, and remain cool, detached, and impersonal. But could she spend an evening with Clint and stay cool and impersonal?

Wide-eyed, Lisa leaned forward and gazed at her reflection in the mirror. Her blue eyes, fringed with thick lashes, her neat hairdo, and her immaculate dress all hinted at composure.

Clint would find quite a different wife from the one

he had left behind. She resolved to see to it that he realized that fact immediately.

With a wry grin she whispered, "Nuts!" It wasn't really important how things appeared to a man she intended to divorce, but she couldn't help wanting everything to be perfect, to show Clint how well she had managed without him.

The doorbell interrupted her reverie. With one more quick glance at her reflection, Lisa smoothed the flawless skirt and headed for the entryway.

chapter 3

SHE OPENED THE DOOR, and Clint entered, along with a blast of cold north wind. Flakes of snow covered the shoulders of his dark coat. Reflected light from the yellow glass hanging lamp cast a soft glow, highlighting the flat planes of his face.

When they both closed the door, his hand covered hers on the knob. His nearness was overwhelming. Lisa gazed up into cool gray eyes and pulled her hand from beneath his.

"Clint, you've changed." The words came out in a breathless whisper. "I think you're even taller."

With a hungry look in his eyes, he spoke huskily. "You're beautiful, Lisa."

His words jolted her into wary alertness. She stepped away quickly. "Come in a moment while I get my coat. It wasn't snowing when I came home from work." She talked more rapidly than usual, speaking of the weather, trying to instill a degree of casualness into the situation. Clint hadn't lost the knack of making the simplest statement sound sensual.

She hurried to the bedroom and scooped up a gray woolen coat, knitted cap, mittens, and muffler. When she returned to the living room, his back was to her, and he was gazing at something in his hands. He turned and glanced at her.

He smiled. "I'm glad you kept this."

She gazed at the paperweight and recalled the moment

they had passed the tiny shop and she had seen it in the window. They had been at Lake Tenkiller, on their honeymoon. When she had stopped to look at the paperweight, Clint had taken her hand and stepped inside to buy it for her. Later she remembered lying in his arms after making love. He had reached out and picked up the globe to hold it above his bare chest and watch the tiny flakes swirl inside the glass. With a hint of merriment in his husky voice he had asked when she was going to show her gratitude for the present. Instantly she had locked her arms around his neck and kissed him, which had led to renewed lovemaking. Later, during the year, he would pick up the globe and, with a twinkle, ask if she was still grateful for his gift.

Sharply, she pulled her thoughts from memories. "I'm ready, Clint," she stated, and swung her coat up to slip into it.

Instantly he replaced the paperweight, and stepped over to help her. She shrugged into the coat and felt his fingers against the nape of her neck as he lifted her hair over the collar.

Without looking at him, Lisa thanked him and moved quickly away. She paused in front of the mirror to adjust the knit cap on her head. Clint's reflection appeared behind hers.

She yanked on mittens and tossed the muffler around her neck, then reached for the door. With a howl, a gust of air whipped snowflakes into her face. Lisa turned and locked the door. Clint took her hand, and they rushed toward the dark Ferrari parked at the curb.

Within moments they were moving smoothly into traffic along the freeway. Clint handled the car adeptly, weaving through the flow of vehicles until they reached a restaurant that was fashioned after an old English tavern.

A fire blazed in the hearth, its warmth delighting Lisa. In a darkened corner Clint held a wing chair for her while she sat down. When he faced her across the table, Lisa took a good look at him.

The gaunt, boyish frame of the young man who had left for Peru had filled out. Dressed in a high-necked black sweater and gray slacks, his broad, powerful shoulders and chest would make him noticeable in any crowd. Thick black hair curled damply over his forehead. In spite of his rugged features, at one time Lisa had considered Clint the most handsome man in the world. Now she wondered if he were not one of the most commanding. It would be impossible to ignore him; yet, for his size, he moved with surprising grace.

A waiter greeted them, and placed menus before them. Lisa studied hers a moment, then glanced at Clint as he asked. "Steak, medium-rare, baked potato with sour cream, salad, coffee—is that right, Lisa?"

She smiled. "Yes." She closed the menu and waited while Clint ordered steaks and Cabernet Sauvignon wine.

Settling back, Clint regarded her with an unwavering contemplation that was disturbing.

"I was sorry to read that your father died," she said.

"It was quick. He was playing golf when he had the attack, and he was gone before the ambulance reached the hospital." He paused a moment. "While I was here for the funeral, I called you several times, but, according to your secretary, you were out of town."

"I had taken a week's vacation and gone to Mexico with friends. I didn't get word until the day of the funeral." She looked down at her hands.

"I wrote you, Lisa, and thanked you for the flowers. Why didn't you answer?"

She glanced at him. "It seemed rather pointless."

His gray eyes darkened, and she wondered if she had made him angry. He spoke in an impassive tone, and it was impossible to guess his feelings. "I'm sorry Dad didn't know you, Lisa."

She stared at Clint in surprise as she remembered the

one meeting with the elder Callaway. "I did see him once, while you were gone." The memory was still painful and humiliating. She looked at Clint and wondered if he had known about it. "He offered me a settlement if I would give you a divorce."

Clint's eyes narrowed. Lisa felt her cheeks flame, and she looked down at her hands. Why did he always have such power to disturb her by a mere glance?

"I'll be damned," he murmured under his breath. "When did he do that?"

"Right after you left for Peru." She looked at him with curiosity. "You didn't know anything about it?"

"No," he growled forcefully. They waited quietly while the waiter poured two glasses of clear red wine. As soon as they were alone, Clint asked, "Why didn't you accept his offer, Lisa?"

She shrugged and looked away, unable to meet his eyes. She stared at the fire and replied, "I guess I can be stubborn too."

"Lisa, how much was it?"

She turned her head and met Clint's gaze, reluctant to reveal the amount. He repeated the question insistently. "How much?"

She told him and drew a sharp breath as he swore again. "Lisa, I never sent you so much as a dollar all the time I was gone. Why didn't you accept Dad's offer?"

She looked down and ran her finger along the smooth, cool stem of the wine glass. "Clint, that was a long time ago. I didn't marry you for your money. I didn't want to accept your father's offer. It wasn't so terrible to have to make it on my own. As a matter of fact, I got a lot of satisfaction out of it."

He shifted and looked at her intently. "You've achieved quite a bit of success and fame."

Although she answered with a laugh, his comment gave her a swift rush of pleasure. "I don't know about any 'fame.'"

"Oh, come on, Lisa. Oklahoma City has had one woman mayor; there's a rumor that you'd like the city to have another."

She sipped her wine and replaced the glass on the table. "That's ridiculous, Clint. I'm not interested in politics."

"Politics are rather heavily involved in the outcome of the highway and lake."

She merely shrugged. "I don't intend to run for mayor."

He swallowed some wine, then regarded her. "You'll get a lot of publicity over this lake matter."

She faced him squarely. "I'm not doing this for publicity." She smiled. "Anyway, at twenty-five, I'm too young to be mayor."

He shrugged. "You could be laying the groundwork for the future. Already you have a great deal in your favor."

Her curiosity was aroused. "What do I have in my favor except a small amount of notice from this?"

"You've risen almost to the top of your Department You were chosen 'Outstanding Woman of the Year' by the Chamber of Commerce last December, because of your efforts to conserve Oklahoma's resources. You headed a successful campaign to save wild cedars from blight. You helped establish the Southwest Historical Tour with your fund-raising drives, and you've been guest lecturer at several organizations. . . ."

She regarded him with dismay. "How did you find out that information?"

"It wasn't difficult. At the same time, you have a private life that you've managed to keep very private."

Suddenly the conversation was on dangerous ground. To get the subject off herself, Lisa asked, "How does it feel to be back home?"

One dark eyebrow arched. "Are you interested in politics?" he insisted.

A flash of anger warmed Lisa's cheeks. "Clint, my life is my business, not yours!"

He smiled. "All I'm doing, Lisa, is asking a question that many people in this city will ask sooner or later."

His persistence was needling her. She clamped her lips together and debated whether or not to answer, then said, "I have no political ambitions."

They remained silent while the waiter placed chilled salads with creamy dressing before them.

After the first few bites, Clint said, "Why do you keep your private life so confidential?"

"Clint, have you hired a detective? Is that how you found out where I live?"

He shook his head. "No. I've merely made some inquiries."

She placed her fork on her plate. "It's really none of your business!"

He looked into her eyes and replied softly, "I need to know my opposition."

Lisa clenched her fists in her lap for a moment then calmly resumed eating her salad. She refused to let him goad her into a display of anger. She would never admit that little was known about her private life because most of her time and efforts had been spent in achieving success at work.

"Would you fill me in on the details about the lake, Lisa?" Clint asked.

She glanced at him. "I suspect you're already aware of everything there is to know about it."

There was a quick flash of annoyance in his eyes as he asked, "Would you please go over the information?"

She obliged by replying, "Your father was in charge at the time bids were placed. When Charles Mallory became president, after your father's heart attack, he called and asked me to stop criticism of the proposed highway. He said it was an embarrassment for the company."

Clint tilted his head to one side. "How did this lake get to be so dear to your heart?"

"As a matter of fact, if I weren't working in conservation," she replied candidly, "I don't know if I'd have given a thought to a new highway. Until you get closely involved with these things, you know little about them."

Clint finished his salad and leaned back. His gray eyes were thoughtful. "When you're not fighting city hall and the highway department, what else do you do?"

"My job is assistant director of the public relations office of the Conservation Department. Mostly, I write publications for our Department. Also, I write reports on conservation efforts taken regarding state projects."

"Is that how you got involved in Lake Dodson?" he asked.

She nodded. "It's routine to compile information on the effects of the highway and what steps are being taken in the interest of conserving resources. We gather facts about the impact on the area. Various people—those involved in the project, councilmen, engineers, the public—use this information."

"You said you write publications. What kind?"

"I do articles for brochures and pamphlets about conservation in those same areas. My department is in charge of conserving our state's resources and preserving its important sites. I just finished a brochure about the Heavener Runestone, which may provide evidence of Viking explorations to 'Vinland,' which was their word for North America, and it could date back to 1010. My department wants to make certain that area is preserved."

"Isn't that near Poteau?"

Thankful to have the conversation on safer ground, she replied, "Yes, in a state park. There are carvings like that in other places, too. This particular one is on a huge stone twelve feet tall. Vikings used runic alphabets, beginning around 200 A.D. and lasting until 1200 A.D. The Heavener Runestone has eight carved runes."

The waiter appeared with thick, buttered steaks and fluffy potatoes in foil jackets. Lisa spread sour cream over the steaming baked potato. "It has nothing to do with my job for the state," she added, "but I also write articles on Oklahoma for a local publication. I'm a contributing editor. Right now, I'm doing a series of articles on scenic areas in the state. In the next few weeks I'll go to the Glass Mountains, in the western part of Oklahoma."

Clint took a bite of steak and glanced at her. "Why do all that, Lisa? Doesn't your job keep you busy?"

She shrugged. "It brings in extra income. I get additional information for my work, and it's interesting."

He studied her. "Hmmm. Sounds like you might be overworked, Lisa. Not trying to keep busy to fill a void, are you?"

She glanced at him sharply. "No."

Clint continued to gaze at her. "Who did you have a date with last night?"

Lisa paused, then answered, "I told you yesterday, Clint, that it's none of your business."

"I suppose I should have known better, but it's still a shock to come home and find that my wife is going out on a date."

She placed her fork on her plate and looked at him squarely. "Clint, you said you wanted to discuss the highway. Otherwise there is nothing for us to say, except possibly to discuss a divorce."

Surprisingly, he yielded. "Okay, during dinner we'll keep the conversation limited to jobs and lakes."

She took a deep breath, then cut another piece of steak and raised a succulent bite to her mouth.

"What will the highway do to the lake, Lisa?"

She swallowed. "If you want facts and figures, I don't have them with me, but in general, it will disturb wildlife and harm the ecology of the area. You know it will destroy the peace and beauty of the lake."

He shrugged. "It's a large lake and quickly becoming a lone spot of water in the center of a large metropolitan area. Whether the highway is there or not, don't you think it's only a matter of time before the area is developed?"

"A quiet residential area would never be as destructive as a major highway," she insisted.

"Lisa, you're on quite a campaign against this, yet you say you can't give me any facts and figures. . . ."

She felt a swift stab of annoyance. "Clint, I have them at the office."

"May I see them?"

"Certainly."

"I'll pick you up for lunch tomorrow, and you can bring them along. How's that?"

She hesitated only for an instant, then nodded. She leaned forward. "Clint, it's a huge lake. We've fished there. It's quiet and peaceful, and lots of birds come to feed in it. A highway will destroy that. Our city needs to look ahead to protect these places. . . ."

He leaned forward, and his hand brushed her cheek. "I wish I had as much of your interest as that lake does."

She caught her breath and suffered a pang that was almost like a physical blow. "Oh, Clint, don't open up old wounds. . . ." she whispered. She pressed back against the seat and spoke quickly. "I have to get home, Clint." In desperation, she threw out the only thing that she knew would save her from an onslaught of Clint's charm. "Tom said he'd call."

Clint straightened, and his gray eyes changed to flint. "Lisa, are you in love with this man?"

chapter 4

FOR AN INSTANT she looked down at her hands. If she answered in the affirmative, Clint would stop making personal remarks. She'd be protected from another heartbreak.

She raised her head. It was impossible to gaze into his wide, piercing eyes and not be truthful. Her gaze slid away, and she murmured, "I don't know...." A twinge of guilt rocked her, and the ironic fact flitted through her mind that Tom Perkins would be shocked if he knew the turn their conversation was taking.

"Is this man the reason you didn't answer my letters?"

She looked up in surprise. Anger pierced her and brought a forthright answer. "I didn't answer the first three letters you wrote because I was furious when you left."

He faced her steadily and after a moment's silence said, "Okay. That's the first three. Why didn't you answer the others?"

"I saw your picture, Clint, in a magazine. You were with a beautiful South American actress. She's probably not the only woman you've taken out since you left here either, is she?"

It was a guess, but it hit the mark. A red flush crept up his cheeks. "Lisa, I'm no monk. I've had dates, but they didn't mean anything...."

"You had your arm around her in the picture." Lisa

sensed a stirring of the fury she had felt when she had discovered the picture.

"Look, you sent me packing. You wouldn't go with me to Peru, then you wouldn't answer my letters. I'm only human, Lisa."

"That wasn't long after you went down there, Clint. Wouldn't it be stupid for me to hang on every letter while you were out having a good time?"

He leaned forward, and his gray eyes flashed with fire. "You haven't been sitting home alone with the television while I was gone either! You date, yet it makes you madder than a wet hen for me to do so!"

"You hardly looked like the languishing husband, Clint. She was very beautiful."

He held up both hands. "I'm not dating her now, Lisa."

"Clint, this is useless. I need to get home."

With an easy movement he rose, then came around to hold her chair. As she walked by his side, Lisa once again realized how much he had changed physically.

She caught oblique glances and outright appraisal from women who noticed Clint. At the door he held Lisa's coat, then slipped into his own.

When they stepped outside, snow was falling in huge, feathery flakes, swirling in a silent, magical beauty that transformed ordinary shapes into mysterious white abstractions.

Clint looked down at her. "I'm parked at the end of the lot. If you'd like, I'll pick you up here."

She shook her head. "No, this is beautiful." She lifted her face to the snow and felt pinpoints of ice.

"It's not only beautiful," he replied, "it's also fun." He leaned down and scooped up fistfuls of snow.

Incredulously, Lisa watched. "Clint! Don't you dare!"

A devilish grin was his only answer. Out of self-preservation, Lisa backed away. "Don't you dare throw that snow at me!"

He laughed. "You won't melt."

He reached for her, and Lisa turned to run to the car. The snowball splattered against her shoulder.

She reached the car but found it locked. She turned, and another snowball came sailing toward her. Lisa yelled and ducked, then scooped up a handful of snow as Clint approached the car. She flung it at him and watched it splash across his chest.

"Aha!" He scooped up another handful and advanced.

"Truce!" Lisa cried, laughing helplessly.

He reached her and gazed down at her. His voice was soft. "That's more like you, Lisa. You never used to be as solemn as you were tonight."

"Maybe I didn't have reason to be solemn then."

"Honey . . ."

"Clint, it's getting cold. Will you unlock the car, please?"

Without a word he did as she asked, and waited until she was seated before closing the door. He moved to the opposite side and slid beneath the wheel.

Even though the snow was getting deep, the car clung to the road, and they made swift progress along the deserted streets.

Lisa listened to the steady swish of the windshield wipers and the soft crunch of snow beneath the tires. All at once she realized they weren't heading in the direction of her apartment. She glanced at him. "Where are we going?"

"I thought we might look at the lake."

"Clint, you're crazy!"

He shrugged one shoulder and shook out a pack of cigarettes. He glanced at her. "Do you smoke, Lisa?"

She shook her head. "When did you start?"

"While I was in Peru."

"Clint, we'll get stuck in the snow. The lake is no place to be in a snowstorm."

"We won't get stuck. Don't be so cautious." He

glanced at her. "You said you expect a call. Do you have a date later?"

"No." She shook her head and watched him uneasily. He exhaled, and a wisp of smoke drifted above his head. Clint watched the road and cracked open his window a fraction to allow the smoke to escape. His features were impassive; it was impossible to tell what he was thinking.

Lisa knew it was useless to argue about going to the lake. Short of leaping from the car, she was at the mercy of his arrogant whims. She settled back against the seat and rode in silence.

They reached the lake road and turned. Their headlights caught the darkness of water. Clint drove toward the docks, then entered a parking lot next to a dock. When he cut the motor, silence descended.

For a moment Lisa was aware of the swirling white flakes that surrounded them, enveloping them in an intimate closeness.

The interior of the car was warm; the windows were beginning to frost. Lisa scooted against the door and turned to face Clint. His knee brushed hers, and she shifted away.

"You see, Clint, if there were a highway here, you wouldn't have this undisturbed silence."

"That's true." He puffed the cigarette, then squinted against the smoke as he peered at her. "Lisa, you know, even if you convince me we shouldn't have this highway, there's nothing I can do to stop the work. All I can do is give up my contract. The city will simply hire someone else to do the job."

"It would go against your own best interests to oppose the highway," she answered quickly. "So if you did, people would listen. You could draw more attention and gain far more support than anyone else." She pulled off her mittens and laid them on the seat. "Callaway and Associates is so large that you wouldn't really suffer if you gave up this contract."

He regarded her solemnly and shook his head. "I don't know about that. There's a lot of money involved, Lisa, and many people are depending on the work." He leaned forward and stubbed out his cigarette, closed the ashtray, and cocked his head to one side to study her. "Is this the first public project you've opposed?"

"Yes," she answered.

For an instant his lips tightened. "Are you certain you're not biased because of personal matters?"

"Not at all!" she answered with indignation. "I'm not doing this to cause your company trouble or to spite you. What would be the point in that?"

He shrugged. "If you mean that, then let's drop it. I'm glad to hear it isn't a personal grudge."

"It's not."

Suddenly changing the subject, he asked, "Would you like to see a picture of what I worked on in Peru?"

"Yes," she replied, and watched as he leaned across her and opened the glove compartment. His arm rested on her knee, and she remained perfectly quiet, as if she did not notice, but her skin tingled with an aggravating awareness of every ounce of pressure he exerted. He scooted closer and turned on the interior light, then slipped open a manila envelope.

As he withdrew the pictures, he glanced down at her and, with a mocking, exaggerated leer, asked, "My darling, would you care to see my etchings?"

Lisa laughed and looked at the pictures. The first was a breathtaking view of a highway built into rugged mountains, with large spans supporting flaring curves of steel.

"This must have been horrendous to build."

"It was," he answered simply. He placed the picture on the bottom of the stack, and she glanced at the next. Clint leaned close. His fingers brushed hers as he pointed. "This is before we began. Our camp was here."

Suddenly she was aware of him pressed against her side, his breath lightly stirring her hair when he talked, his fingers touching hers. She looked at the next picture. It was of Clint, stripped to the waist, a yellow hard hat on his head, with bronzed shoulders glistening in the sunlight, his chest dark with a mat of hair. His jeans were low on his narrow hips, and his hand rested on his waist.

"A Peruvian jungle rat," he stated, and she smiled. As he faced into the camera, his white teeth showed in a wide smile. It was impossible not to notice the powerful biceps and trim body.

"Did you work along with the crew?" she asked.

His tone was grim as he replied, "Every minute of every day."

She glanced at him, then looked at the next picture. While she studied a fountain surrounded by beautiful flowers, Clint reached across with his left hand and started the motor, to keep the heater running. "That place particularly appealed to me. The picture shows the patio of one of the hotels where I stayed."

"It's lovely," she remarked, then wondered if someone had stayed there with him. Was the actress in the background, out of sight of the camera? Impatient with herself, Lisa stirred uncomfortably.

What was she doing, sitting in such a deserted place, going over Clint's pictures as if they were important to her? She flipped quickly past the next two pictures, then stopped when another caught her attention. It was a high mountain peak with steps cut into the side, and other jagged peaks lower in the background, all covered in thick, lush green beneath a dazzling blue sky.

"How gorgeous!" she breathed.

"Machu Picchu," came a cryptic reply, and she looked at him.

"What is that?"

"The last stronghold of the Incas. Over eight thousand feet in altitude, in the clouds, it's unbelievable until you see it for yourself."

"It looks awesome."

"We think we're such builders," he mused, "then we come across something like that. Centuries old, more than two hundred buildings made of unmortared stone, constructed in terraces. It's impossible to imagine how they did the work without modern tools and equipment. Impossible to think of climbing those steps that might as well hang in open air. One misstep, and you fall thousands of feet. You can look down on clouds and birds."

The next four snapshots were of the same site. As Lisa looked at them, Clint covered her hands with his in a quick, impersonal gesture. "You're still cold."

"I'm fine," she replied, but he dropped his arm around her shoulder and pulled her close against him while he pointed out a line of stones in the picture.

"They think the Incas fled to this inaccessible, remote place from Cuzco to escape persecution by the Spaniards."

His breath was warm against her ear. His hand shifted and covered hers again. Then he reached up to twist a tendril of hair into place behind her ear. With every movement his hands brushed lightly against her ear, then along her cheek then at the nape of her neck.

Lisa was afraid to tell him to stop, because she didn't want him to realize his touch disturbed her. His hands were light, casual, while he spoke in an impassive voice about his pictures. She was uncertain of whether he was even aware of what he was doing, but she was growing more acutely conscious of it by the second.

Every contact was electrifying, disturbing, alarming. With the barest of touches he could still stir all the longings that he used to arouse so easily.

Finally she could take no more. "Clint, please . . ."

His face was only inches away. He regarded her solemnly. "Please what, honey?"

His gaze drifted to her lips. Confused emotions ran

through Lisa—anger that Clint would act so innocent of knowledge of what he was deliberately doing, fright at her own reactions, and . . . her mind refused to acknowledge any more. She took a deep breath.

"Clint . . ." It was impossible to speak. She looked at his finely textured skin, the firm, mobile mouth that she knew so well.

He leaned forward. His lips met hers, and a fierce current coursed through her. His arms closed around her.

His strong arms held her firmly. She felt intoxicated by his kiss. With desperation she pushed, but it seemed as if all the strength was burned out of her arms. His kiss curled her toes and set her pulse hammering.

Finally he shifted, then moved his lips against her cheek. "Lisa, we don't need a divorce. You don't know how I've missed you."

chapter 5

"CLINT," SHE BEGAN to protest, but gasped at a wild tingling when he kissed her throat, her neck. Then his hands were against her nape, and suddenly the barret was gone. Her golden hair tumbled over her shoulders, and he leaned back to look at her.

He exhaled sharply and whispered, "That's the way your hair should be." His work-roughened fingers grazed her lips lightly. "Your mouth is red from my kiss; the hair that I've dreamed of should never be confined." The huskiness in his tone deepened. "The only thing needed to complete the picture is for that dress to be gone." He groaned and reached for her.

Lisa twisted sharply and squeezed against the door. "Clint, stop, please."

He paused and gazed down at her.

She looked away. "Take me home. Nothing has changed."

"You're damn right," he murmured. "Lisa, one kiss, and you set me on fire. I need you. I want you desperately. I love you...."

She struggled to hold him away. "Clint, you made your choice when you walked out on me and went to Peru."

His chest heaved in a long sigh, and he turned away to look at the whiteness outside. After a moment he faced her. "Lisa, you're the one who walked out."

"Clint, I loved you with all my heart when we got

31

married, then suddenly you had to go to Peru to take over that division of the company for your father and you demanded that I give up everything to go with you."

His voice was grating. "Lisa, one of us had to give things up. I happen to have some old-fashioned ideas—that I'll grant—that the wife should give up her job before the husband." He shrugged. "Maybe not always, but in our circumstances, it seemed the right thing to do. I had little choice, unless I wanted to give up my inheritance and work for a competitor of my father's." He gazed thoughtfully into space. "I didn't know then that Dad would offer you money to get a divorce. He told me the Peruvian office was about to fold. I was ordered to take it over or get out for good." Clint's head turned, and he studied her. "Now that I know about the offer of money, I realize that he might have issued the ultimatum to me to break up our marriage."

She spoke in a small voice. "It looks as if he achieved what he wanted without spending a dime." She turned the mittens in her lap. "Clint, I was just getting started, and I needed my job. I had to see if I could succeed." She looked up, and it was difficult to get out the words. "We're right back at the same old stalemate."

"Dammit!" he exploded. "I wish to hell you felt about me the way I do about you!"

Every breath was painful. She felt as if her heart were shattering into fragments. "I could say the same, Clint. You do want things your way."

His gray eyes flashed with anger, and a muscle worked in his jaw. "I want you, Lisa." He grasped her shoulders, his brow furrowed in a frown. "Lisa, I'm ..." He paused as if searching for the right word. He swore and pulled her to him to kiss her passionately.

With a cry she wrenched herself away. She opened the door and jumped out. Quickly she began marching away through the snow.

In an instant he was out of the car and by her side.

He placed his hand on her arm. "Lisa, please...let's discuss this."

She whirled to face him. "Clint, you've been involved with other women. Don't come home and turn to me as if I mean something special." When he made a quick gesture with his hand and started to speak, she added, "There's no need to go over it all again. It's done and behind us, but when you left, I wasn't certain I'd survive."

He took another step closer and reached for her, grasping both arms, but Lisa's hands came up against his, and she protested, "Don't, Clint! At least let me finish. It's been dreadful, but I did recover. I don't want to get hurt another time. If I let you make love to me now, I'll be lost, and ultimately things will come around to another decision and it will be necessary to do things your way or get hurt. Either take me home or I'll walk."

"Dammit, you can't walk home from here! Lisa, you have a streak of stubbornness.... Will you please listen?"

She jerked free and turned away. She had taken only a few steps when he said, "Come on, I'll take you home."

Wordlessly, she turned and looked at him. An angry scowl was on his face. "Won't you even discuss things with me?" he asked.

"Clint, every discussion ends up with me in your arms."

"And is that so terrible? Lisa, I'll stand right here. There's three feet of snow between us. I don't want a divorce. I think we can work out our differences. I love you as much as I did when I left—"

"Clint, it's useless," she interrupted. "I've made a new life for myself, and you're not part of it."

A tense silence stretched between them.

"Okay, I won't touch you, but how about a truce? Let's forget the past and future, take each day one at a time, and reacquaint ourselves with each other. No more serious discussions for a time. Okay?"

She studied him intently. Behind him was the lake. Snow fell on Clint's black hair and dark shoulders. It was bright enough to see clearly flakes caught on his lashes.

Not strong enough to refuse, and knowing she was opening herself up to more pain, Lisa nodded. "Very well."

"Good," he answered softly. "May I hold your hand?"

She had to laugh. For someone as sensuous, suave, and sophisticated as Clint, his request sounded ridiculous.

"Yes," she replied, and offered her hand.

He took it and smiled at her, and Lisa had to repress a sudden desire to fling herself into his arms. Together they headed toward the car. He paused and looked around. "Isn't this beautiful?"

Before she could answer, he glanced down. "C'mon, let's make angels in the snow."

He flounced down and moved his arms back and forth. "Did you ever do this when you were a kid?"

She laughed. "Yes, and got a great deal of snow down my neck."

"Go ahead," he urged. "It won't hurt your neck."

Laughing, Lisa sank down on her back. She squealed as drops of ice melted against her skin. Quickly she moved her arms up and down before Clint rose and reached down to pull her to her feet.

He released her hand immediately and studied their imprints in the snow. "Mine looks as if an elephant fell down."

He began to roll a snowball. "This is good, wet stuff— excellent for snowmen." For the next half hour they worked diligently, until they had constructed a large snowman. Clint found a log and broke off two slender branches for arms. Finally he rummaged in the car to produce a battered cap, a rope that he tied around the neck, sunglasses, and an orange golf ball for a nose.

He used his pocketknife to cut another length of rope to tie around the middle. Lisa watched while his head was bent in concentration. Her throat grew tight, and she longed to brush her hands along his cheek. Desperately, she scooped up snow and patted it against the snowman.

Clint placed the rope around the snowman and a remaining short length for a smiling mouth, then he surveyed the work.

"There! He belongs in a museum, as a work of art."

Lisa laughed. "He's ridiculous, but he's definitely noteworthy for size. That's the largest snowman I've ever seen."

"Well, we'll leave him in solitude, but before we go, I'll dub him with a good Peruvian name—Pedro Chosica."

Lisa's voice was filled with amusement. "I don't think Pedro Chosica will ever compete with 'Frosty.'"

Clint dropped his arm casually across her shoulders, and they headed for the car. He held open the door, then climbed in. For one fleeting moment the wheels spun. Clint shifted to reverse, the car moved a few inches, then he shifted again, and they were free.

Lisa watched his hands on the steering wheel and thought about the competency in his fingers. Clint could build almost anything. They had filled their apartment with furniture he had built. What was a hobby would have been a vocation, had he been born in different circumstances. She realized with relief that she no longer felt overwhelmed by his abilities.

Too easily she could recall her own feelings of inadequacy around her brother and brilliant parents. All three were perfectionists who drove themselves. Her father had been a research chemist, her mother a college professor of botany, and her brother a chemistry professor. Lisa's thoughts were interrupted by Clint.

"What are you thinking?" he asked.

"I was remembering my family."

He glanced at her. "I hope you've gotten over your feelings of guilt."

She shrugged. "I have. Or at least, I don't think about it in the same way. At the time, it seemed terrible that they died in a hotel fire and I escaped, when they had so much to offer the world and I had so little."

"That's absurd," he stated gruffly. He took out a cigarette and lit it, then exhaled while he opened the window slightly. "Lisa, maybe that's why it was so important to you to prove your own abilities to yourself."

She glanced at him, and for a brief moment they looked at each other, before he turned back to the road.

"It probably has been," she replied quietly, "but that knowledge hasn't lessened my need to do so."

She glanced at him once more. She longed to reveal to him that his own capabilities were almost as awesome as her family's had been. When she had started with the Department, it had seemed imperative that she prove she could do the job well. She struggled to find the right words to tell Clint, but before she could, the moment was gone.

"When are you going to the Glass Mountains?" he asked.

She looked out the window. "Not until the snow melts and the roads are clear. I should have gone this week, so I'll go the first chance I get."

"My knowledge about this state is limited to colleges, cities, and highways, particularly the eastern part of Oklahoma. I don't know anything about the Glass Mountains."

"They're a part of the early geological history of the state," Lisa stated. "They were formed by an inland sea, some two hundred million years ago."

The car slowed, then stopped in front of her apartment. Clint let the motor idle and turned to face her. "Do you need a driver to take you to the Glass Mountains?"

"Clint, right now we have several inches of snow on the ground. I can't go this week. Let's do what you suggested earlier—take each moment as it comes."

He shrugged. "Okay." He leaned toward her. When she started to speak, he stopped within inches of her and smiled, holding up both hands. "I'm not touching you." He was not, but his nearness was as disturbing as a touch. "In spite of the tiff," he said easily, "I've had a good time tonight. Maybe we made progress. Thank you for going with me."

She laughed. "I think I'm the one who's supposed to do the thanking, since you took me to a delicious dinner."

"You have changed," he remarked.

"I'm not certain I want to hear how," she stated.

He smiled and tapped her chin with his finger in a brief, impersonal gesture. "It's not bad. You're more poised and certain of yourself."

She tried to keep her voice light. "Thank you, Clint. That comes from working, I'm certain."

He sobered and his voice lowered. "And you look as if you're holding a whole bunch of things bottled up inside you that ought to come out."

She looked down at her hands. "That isn't anything very different, Clint. It's always been difficult for me to express my feelings."

Lisa did not add that in the past, Clint had been the only person she had ever known who she felt free to talk to. It had been easy to express her feelings to him, but until she had met him she had never been able to do that with anyone.

"I'm really glad things are going so well for you, Lisa."

She raised her head to thank him again and was surprised to catch a frown of concern on his face. Suddenly she wanted to blurt out that it was ridiculous for him to sound solicitous, when he had so quickly abandoned her to go to Peru and pursue his own career.

Instead, she merely continued, "The only problem I have at my job concerns Lake Dodson."

"That doesn't actually affect your job, does it?" he asked, with such swiftness that she was startled.

She shook her head. "No."

"Is your supervisor putting pressure on you to do this?"

"No, Clint. It's my own doing. I've come to feel very strongly about preserving some of the areas around this state." She turned in the seat. "I'd better go in. I have to get up early in the morning."

He got out and came around to hold open her door. Together they walked to her apartment, and she turned to face him. "It was fun, Clint."

He took her hands in his. "I feel like I'm back in high school. How about one good-night kiss?"

One kiss was all he asked, yet his gray eyes were devouring her with a hunger that made her knees weak. It would be absurd to refuse one kiss. It was impossible to say no. She raised her face.

Because of his expertise she was unaware of the moment when he had unbuttoned her coat. He stepped nearer. His arms went beneath her coat and pressed her to him. Instead of kissing her immediately, he gazed into her eyes.

His voice was husky. "You'll never know how many times I've wanted you in my arms."

It was difficult to breathe. She was aware of every inch of his long, lean body, which was rock-hard, pressed against her. She looked at his lips, so close to hers. She wanted them on hers, wanted Clint with all the familiar, pent-up yearnings she had fought against for so long.

"You're gorgeous, Lisa." He buried his face in her long hair and murmured close to her ear, "No woman on earth has hair like this. I know it."

"Clint," she whispered, then was silent as he turned.

With disarming lightness his lips grazed hers, then her cheek, before returning again to her mouth in a tantalizing, feathery touch that changed to a probing, velvety warmth that was impossible to resist.

The wind, the swirling, cold flakes of snow diminished to nothing next to the storm of his kiss. Clinging to his granite shoulders as if they were the only solid thing in the world, Lisa's rational thoughts were as blanketed and obliterated as the traffic signs, fences, and objects around her were by snow.

All the little warning signals, collected defenses, were banished in a blinding flurry of responses.

His hand pressed the curve at the small of her back, tilting her hips against him. Across the nape of her neck his other hand moved with the swirling lightness of snow, yet it was warm and vital, evoking tingling sensations.

Tender caresses and his prolonged kiss were numbing her objections, erasing from her consciousness anything except awareness of his mouth on hers.

A small voice in the back of her mind kept asking, Why? Why could Clint stir her so much? No one else could do this. It wasn't fair. . . .

He released her. It was an effort for her to open her eyes. Heavy-lidded, she gazed up at him. Her lips tingled, and it was difficult to breathe. Flakes of snow melted against her cheeks. Wind tore at her hair, yet she was oblivious to it.

Clint held out his hand. "Give me your key, and I'll unlock the door." Only the throaty huskiness of his voice betrayed that he felt anything.

She did as he instructed, and watched while he opened the door. He switched on a hall light, then returned the key. "I'll see you tomorrow at noon. I'll pick you up at work."

She stepped inside and faced him. A muscle worked in his jaw. While his stance appeared relaxed, his knuckles as he gripped the doorknob were white.

Finding it difficult to talk, Lisa could hardly bear to say goodbye. "Good night, Clint."

He nodded and turned into the wind. He did not bend against it, but raised his face and let the gusts sweep through his hair as he crossed to his car in long, firm strides. Before he slid into the Ferrari, he paused and looked back at her over its top, then waved.

Lisa waved in return and whispered, "Clint..." Sudden tears stung her eyes, then regret filled her. She switched off the lights and headed for her room. She shouldn't have agreed to go out with him in the first place. It had accomplished nothing for her; instead, it had destroyed all the calm she had acquired during his absence.

Had he noticed her response? Did it matter to him? she wondered. Was it flattering to his ego—or did it mean something deeper? Uncertainties and qualms shook her.

She stopped and stared into space. The notion that she still loved him began to surface, but she fought it down. She would not consider it. What she felt for Clint was gone. Tonight had been purely physical. She should have seen other men while he was away....

With a quick shake of her head, she entered the blue-and-white bedroom. Usually she surveyed her room with satisfaction. She loved the soft blue carpet, white French furniture, and white eyelet-embroidered bedspread. But tonight she took little notice of it.

The phone startled her, and she reached for it. "Hi, it's Tom. Sorry to call so late."

"That's all right," she replied.

"I hope so. I debated whether to call. I keep strange hours. I'm at the office right now."

"You do work late!" she exclaimed.

"We had a story. A truckload of pigs turned over on

the Interstate highway, at the downtown exit. No one was hurt—including the pigs—but it made an interesting bit of news. Pigs were everywhere for a while. They're still trying to find all of them."

Lisa laughed. "I'd hate to be chasing little pigs downtown at this hour."

"Lisa, I'd like to take you to dinner tomorrow night."

It was on the tip of her tongue to refuse, but she thought of Clint. She would never get over him if she sat around and didn't go out with anyone else. Still, she was reluctant. She didn't want to use Tom for her own gain.

"I have a few more questions I'd like to ask you," he added.

"I'll be happy to answer your questions, but I have a report to get done. I'd planned to work on—"

"None of that," he interrupted. "You can always work; you can't always eat dinner with me. Do you like fish?"

"Yes," she answered.

"Good." He suggested a time, continued to talk for a few more minutes, then told her good night. Lisa replaced the receiver, then gazed at the phone. She wondered what Clint was doing. His mother had died two years before Lisa had met him, so Lisa had only known his father. It still hurt to recall the shock of his offer of a substantial sum of money to divorce Clint. The elder Callaway had made it clear he thought she had married Clint for his money. Perhaps her stubbornness and hurt over his offer had caused her to feel reluctant ever to get a divorce. She thought of Clint's surprise when she had told him about his father's offer. At least Clint had been unaware of it at the time.

Snatches of their conversation returned to her— Clint's probing question about why she had not answered his letters. She remembered the letters she had written, filled with hurt and anger. She had never mailed them.

Once, she had written a calm, objective reply—and cautiously held on to it before mailing it, to make certain it was what she wanted to say to him. Then she had seen his picture with the actress. She had gone straight home and torn the letter to shreds.

chapter 6

THE NEXT MORNING, when Lisa selected a pale-yellow lamb's-wool sweater and matching woolen skirt, she was thinking of her date at noon with Clint. But once she reached the office, work crowded all thoughts of it out of her mind.

Eileen was discussing a chart of figures with her when the intercom buzzed and Lisa's secretary, Nancy Gates, announced, "Mr. Clint Callaway to see you, Lisa."

Aware of Eileen's gaze resting on her with curiosity, Lisa asked Nancy to send him in.

"He's already in Oklahoma?" Eileen asked.

"Yes," Lisa replied, rummaging in a drawer. She didn't want to discuss Clint's homecoming with Eileen. Before she could say more, the door opened, and Clint entered.

His conservative, dark-blue suit accentuated his deep tan and dark hair. Even dressed like other businessmen, he seemed to fill the office; his powerful build and rugged male features made him appear overwhelming. His impact was not lost on Eileen.

After introductions, Eileen rose, managing to do so with a supple wiggle that fully revealed the voluptuous figure beneath her red jersey. As Eileen reached to gather the charts and pencils on Lisa's desk, she dropped a tablet.

She leaned down to retrieve it at the same moment

43

Clint did, and their hands brushed. Eileen accepted it and straightened to give him a dazzling smile.

"Was it difficult to leave Peru?" she asked.

With a flash of amusement in his eyes, Clint shook his head. "Not one bit." He looked past Eileen to Lisa. "I'm thankful to be home."

Eileen glanced at Lisa. "What a shame you couldn't have gone with him." She turned to Clint again. "Even though you're glad to be home, it must have been a wonderful experience, Mr. Callaway...."

"Clint," he interrupted easily.

"Clint." Eileen continued, "I have an aunt who is planning a trip to Peru. Would you mind if I give her your phone number so she can ask you some questions?"

Clint agreed quickly, and Lisa glanced at Eileen. She had never heard Eileen mention an aunt or make any reference to Peru. Eileen turned a page of the tablet, then took a pencil and jotted down Clint's phone number.

Eileen closed the tablet and smiled. "I wish I could take my vacation in time to go with her." She waved her hand slightly. "I'm not tied to my office, like your wife is. She's a workaholic." Eileen glanced at Lisa. "I'm teasing, Lisa, but you are dedicated. Work always comes first."

There was little she could say, so Lisa merely smiled. Eileen glanced at both of them. "Well, I'll leave you two alone." She extended a hand to Clint. "It was so nice to meet you, Clint. For a long time, now, I've wondered about Lisa's husband. You're not at all what I expected."

Clint let the last remark pass. "I've wondered about her friends," he countered easily. "It was nice to meet you."

Eileen regarded him intently, then turned to Lisa. "I am going, but you know . . . as long as Clint's here . . . Lisa, would you mind if I borrow your husband for just one teensy-weensy moment? There's not a man in this office strong enough to get that cabinet door open. If I ask the janitor, he'll use a crowbar and ruin the finish. Would you mind?"

Eileen looked at Clint, then at Lisa, for their approval. When they both nodded, she slipped her arm through Clint's.

"This won't take a big, strong man like you a second, and I really would appreciate it. I promise to have it filed down so it won't stick again . . ."

Her voice trailed off as she and Clint turned the corner and were out of sight. Lisa sighed and rose to put papers away in the file cabinet. She was just finishing when Clint returned.

He assessed her thoroughly, in a manner as provocative as it was deliberate. Lisa struggled to keep her voice light.

"You made a hit," she stated.

He shrugged. "Where it doesn't count."

"Let me put this folder away, and I'll be ready."

While she did so, Clint moved around the room to study maps on one wall. He drifted over to the opposite wall, gazing at pictures of Oklahoma's state parks and a map of the city's lake. Again he reminded her of a tiger, as he quietly explored the office until he had looked at everything open to view. She closed the bottom drawer of her desk and glanced at him.

Clint leaned one shoulder against a wall, his hands in his pockets and his feet crossed. He appeared totally relaxed, and returned her gaze with his usual directness. He smiled. "I'd like to see Callaway start a house organ, a regular monthly magazine. Maybe I can entice you away from here to take charge of that project, hmmm?"

She smiled. "That might complicate my life too much," she replied, as easily as he had asked.

"Are you ready now? You look pretty."

"Thank you." She had forgotten the quiet thoroughness that surrounded Clint. Little by little, all the things she had tried to forget were returning. Not until the circumstances of choosing between marriage and a career had exploded their life together had there been anything to mar the companionship and wild, wild love between them.

Snatching up the folder of information about Lake Dodson, she picked up her purse and rose to get her coat. Without obvious effort, Clint was at the rack first, holding the gray wool coat for her.

They emerged into a bright, sunshine-filled day. Banks of white snow glistened, but the temperature was climbing, and streets had become slushy. Steadily dripping icicles melted, and water ran from drainspouts. Ankle-deep water flooded part of the parking lot. With Clint's hand lightly at her elbow, Lisa picked her way across the lot until they reached a stream of water pouring through a low spot.

Effortlessly Clint swung her into his arms.

"Clint, I can walk!" Lisa protested.

His white teeth flashed in a teasing grin. "Sure you can, but I intend to have you in my arms any way I can get you, Lisa."

She laughed, and allowed him to carry her, yet she hoped no one in the office saw them. The black Ferrari gleamed as if it had never been near streets of slush. Clint leaned down, opened the door, and deposited her on the seat.

Lisa straightened her skirt and smiled at him as he climbed in.

"Thank you, Sir Galahad."

He gave her a mocking grin. "Thank heaven for large puddles."

"How do you keep this car so clean?"

He twisted to back the car out. "I just had it washed."

For one brief moment, Lisa wondered if he had done so because he was taking her to lunch, then she shrugged away the idea as ridiculous.

"How about a Mexican restaurant?" he asked.

"Fine."

Once they were seated in the gaily decorated restaurant and had ordered, Clint settled back. With a twinkle in his eyes, he stated, "I suspect you haven't read the morning paper."

"I noticed you brought it along," she replied.

"Our friend made the papers."

"Our friend?" Perplexed, she accepted the proffered paper. Beneath headlines concerning the snowstorm was a large picture of the snowman they had built at the lake. She glanced up in surprise, then laughed and studied the caption. "What was it you named him—Pedro?"

"Pedro Chosica," he answered. "Our joint efforts worked pretty well there, Lisa." He reached out and touched her cheek. "At least it made you laugh." He refolded the paper. "Did you bring something for me to study?"

She nodded and produced the folder, opening it to read about the number of migratory birds that passed through Oklahoma and had been spotted at Lake Dodson. Also she read a list of the number of birds known to nest there during each season.

She paused in reading, while the waitress placed a plate of steaming golden nachos before her, then a platter of enchiladas and tacos in front of Clint. He took several bites before laying down his fork and stretching back in the seat. His leg brushed hers, and he shifted away.

"Lisa, do you really feel that a highway alongside the lake will frighten away all of these birds?"

"Yes," she replied solemnly. "Other than persistent sparrows and grackles, most of them will move on. I have figures from other lakes and national reserves to substantiate all this. Car fumes, paving, noise, people— all would contribute to it."

His cool gray eyes rested on her thoughtfully. "Do you have a copy of those figures? I've had so little time to look into this."

"Clint, there are so many birds around the lake—cormorants, grebes, marsh wrens in winter, herons, kingbirds, hummingbirds and phoebes in summer. They mustn't be driven away."

"Next week there's a board meeting about it, among other things." Clint looked at her as if he were about to add something, then shifted, and asked, "If it had been Jones and Henderson or North Engineering who had won the contract, would you still have done the same thing?"

"Yes," she answered emphatically. "I've told you that before, Clint, and I mean it."

"Lisa, I've been told you've asked the City Council to hold another hearing and that they've granted your request. They take it up next week."

She nodded. "That's right. I've pulled together so much more information. Clint, if you'd reconsider Callaway's—"

"Lisa," he interrupted, "I need to study all this." He ran his fingers through his hair; the black curls sprang back with a ripple. "Will you ask them to postpone the hearing for two weeks, to give me time to go over your information?"

"I can't do that!"

"Yes, you can."

A twinge of anger rippled through her. "If I ask them to postpone the hearing and drop my request now, it may be more difficult to rekindle support or interest later. Tom Perkins is writing an article about this. It should come out soon, and will attract a lot of attention."

Lisa sensed his quick anger. "Is Perkins with the paper?"

"Yes."

"Has he worked with you on this all through the campaign?"

She shook her head. "No. Eileen introduced us recently, because he'd learned about my struggle and was interested in doing an article on it."

His eyes narrowed. "You're not getting enthusiastic about this just to please Perkins, are you?"

Her anger deepened. "No," she stated flatly.

"Then why won't you be reasonable about this and let me have some time? Look, you're so concerned about those damn birds—what about the people you'll put out of work if this project is canceled?"

"You know they'll work somewhere else, on another project," she said.

He took a deep breath. "Lisa, they might not. Sometimes there aren't any other projects."

"Then you're not going to help," she said.

He shook his head. "I didn't say that. What I'm asking you to do is give me time to study your facts. Let me have a chance to look into this before I jump into it. I have to consider my company, Lisa. This project involves a great deal of money, and jobs for many people."

"You're asking the one thing that would do the most damage to my case," she replied. Lisa clenched her fists in her lap and stared back at him. Although determined to remain firm, she knew how easily he could twist her around to seeing his viewpoint.

He tilted his head to one side. "Lisa, is it the City Council you're worried about, or Tom Perkins and his publicity for you?"

"I don't care about publicity!" she exclaimed.

"Without knowing for certain what's involved, I can't cast aside my company's interests. You should be able to understand."

"I do, Clint," she answered honestly. "I can see why you hesitate, when you know so little about it, but surely you understand my position. In order to have this hearing I've had to push and solicit support from various people and organizations. It wasn't easy. If I turn around now and say, 'Oh, forget it . . . ' I'll lose my credibility and my backing."

"I'm not asking you to cancel it completely," he

snapped. "I know it's unfortunate, the way things are working out, but please give me time."

Lisa ran her finger along the handle of her coffee cup. What Clint asked was not unreasonable. She could understand why he made the request, yet it would hurt her campaign.

He leaned back and stretched his long legs beneath the table. "Lisa, I want to please you. . . ."

"If it doesn't interfere with what you want," she said.

His gray eyes deepened, and his lips grew firm. They drank coffee in silence for a few minutes; then he said quietly, "According to what you've said, if you wait and get my support, it would be even more helpful."

"Yes, it would," she admitted.

He drank again and motioned to the waitress for a refill. Lisa nodded absentmindedly at her and watched the steaming dark liquid fill the thick yellow mug. She accepted a small pewter pitcher from Clint to pour cream in her cup, then returned the pitcher to him. While she stirred the coffee, she debated the dilemma, thankful that Clint was waiting quietly and allowing her to mull it over without interference.

After a few moments she gazed at him. "The hearing may not make any difference, you know."

"No, it might not. But if you go ahead now, I have no choice but to go in there and oppose what you want. I'll have to support the company or have a hell of a good reason not to."

She finished her coffee in silence. At last, he asked, "Are you ready to leave?"

She nodded, and he rose to come around and hold her coat. They emerged into bright sunshine and strolled toward the car. "Lisa," he continued, "a delay is not that critical. They delay hearings all the time. It's the only possibility if you don't want my opposition."

"Okay, Clint," she agreed, hoping she wouldn't regret her decision.

He squeezed her hand, then released it quickly. "Thanks, honey." He looked down at her with a dazzling smile that made her heart lurch. "You see, we *can* handle disagreements amicably."

"Perhaps it's because there's not as much at stake," she replied.

They reached the car. He held her arm and reached down for the door, but paused. "This slush will be gone and the ground reasonably dry by Saturday. Would you like to drive to the Glass Mountains then?"

She glanced up at him. Cool reason argued that she should refuse his offer. Every minute with him wore down her defenses, made her more vulnerable, because they were evading the issue that had separated them in the first place.

"Perhaps it would be wiser to see our lawyers about the divorce," she replied evenly. A sweep of wind tugged a silky tendril of hair free and curled it across her cheek. Lisa brushed it away and squinted against the sunlight to look at him.

"Let's not rush our fences, Lisa," he said. "How about the Glass Mountains?"

Reluctance and longing divided her and held back an answer. He reached out and curled the tendril around his finger. "Please give me a chance." He tilted her face up. "I know it's not over between us. Sooner or later we're going to have to come to some decisions, but until then, at least give me a chance. I promised to keep my distance—"

"Which you're not doing right now," she interrupted.

He frowned. "I'm not doing anything but talking."

Suddenly she felt foolish. He wasn't even aware of what he was doing, yet his touch was disturbing her.

"Let's go to the Glass Mountains Saturday," he urged.

"All right," she agreed.

"Fine." Another dazzling smile rocked her. Within minutes they were heading back toward her office. As they sped along, Clint asked, "Would you like to visit Pedro Chosica tonight? We could have dinner, then drive out and see how much of him is still standing."

"Thank you, but I can't." She wanted to change the subject, and asked quickly, "Are you staying at your house?"

With wry amusement, he glanced at her. "No. I've put it up for sale. My sister will never leave New York, and she's not the least interested in keeping the house. They have their home on Long Island and the co-op in town. She won't ever return to Oklahoma. I don't want to keep it either." He glanced at her again. "Who's your date with?"

Lisa smoothed out the folds of her coat. "I'm going out to dinner tonight, Clint."

"And you're evading my question right now, Lisa. Who is he?"

"Tom Perkins."

Did she imagine one quick, brief flash of anger in his eyes? Lisa couldn't be certain, and mentally shrugged away the possibility.

"Isn't that beyond getting the facts for a story?" he asked sardonically.

She shrugged. "Maybe."

Clint left her at the office. Lisa remained in the doorway and watched him drive off. Had she let him charm her into making a poor decision? After all the difficulties she had gone through to get a new hearing on the proposed site of the highway, for her to ask for a postponement now might be damaging. Clint's request had seemed sensible. She could understand his reasons. Yet she had an awful feeling she had made a mistake.

chapter 7

THE FEELING INCREASED all through dinner with Tom
that night. She hoped the subject wouldn't come up. Now
she regretted her decision. What had seemed so logical
and reasonable when Clint had presented it to her,
seemed, in retrospect, a foolish choice.

After they'd finished dinner at a seafood restaurant,
Tom asked Lisa to accompany him to the office to read
his story. They parked behind the building, and Tom
greeted the security guard. Inside, in various parts of the
building, they passed people at work. They rode the
elevator, then went down the hall to a large room par-
titioned into several cubicles.

In a corner a man was bent over a typewriter. After
Tom had made the introductions, he led Lisa to another
one of the cubicles.

"Welcome to my office." He shoved papers to one
side, then moved others off a chair. He motioned to Lisa
to sit down, then rummaged in a drawer before sitting
beside her and spreading out two sheets for her to read.
He glanced at her.

"Why the big smile?"

"You said your office was knee-deep in papers. I
thought you were kidding."

He laughed. "I work in complete chaos." He tapped
the paper. "My editor is so enthusiastic about this! He
wants more on the subject."

"Marvelous!" she exclaimed.

"He expects a good response to this," Tom continued. "It's the kind of story that has built this paper, one we can really sink our teeth into. I want to get those pictures."

"Several people I know want to get up a petition to protest construction."

Tom grinned broadly. "That's an excellent idea."

Lisa looked down, worried. She didn't want to dampen Tom's enthusiasm, and she knew it was going to be difficult for her to reveal her promise to Clint to delay the hearing. If it was difficult to tell Tom, how much more so would it be with everyone else? More and more she regretted what she'd done. She brought her thoughts back to Tom and tried to listen to what he was saying.

He reached inside a drawer and produced a folded piece of paper. "Now you'll see why I was so happy to hear you suggest a petition. I started one in the office. Here are your first fifty names."

Gazing at it in amazement, Lisa accepted the paper. "You *have* been busy!" Two sheets were stapled together. Beneath a paragraph that summed up the cause of saving Lake Dodson for wildlife was a long list of names. Lisa scanned them quickly, then looked up.

"This is impressive." She tilted her head to one side. "I'd have expected your name to be first. I don't see it here at all."

"No," he replied casually. "I felt I shouldn't sign it, because of my articles. It might cause difficulty."

Difficulty for whom? Lisa wondered briefly. Did Tom's interest only involve the news story he was getting, and not the issue itself? She studied the list once more, then slipped it into her purse. "I'll have time to work on this, because I agreed to ask the Council to postpone the hearing."

Tom's eyes narrowed. "Why?"

She hated to admit her concession to Clint. Even

though she didn't want to relate their conversation, she felt compelled to explain. "Clint asked me to request a postponement, to give him time to study the situation and make an intelligent decision."

Tom's dark eyes rested on her. Although Lisa felt uncomfortable, she couldn't detect a flicker of disappointment, anger, or any other emotion in his gaze. Tom Perkins hid his feelings very effectively. He spoke quietly.

"Lisa, I can't come between a husband and wife. If you're doing this because you still love—"

"No!" she interrupted with compelling intensity. "His arguments seemed reasonable, and I'd have done the same thing if I'd just met him."

Tom gave her a thin smile. "I doubt it. If you delay the hearing, you'll lose your fight. What good reason can you give people who sign the petition, or the Council or the paper or the public in general?"

"I'm allowing time for the construction engineers to study the situation."

Tom's eyes narrowed. "It sounds pretty lame, I think you'll have to agree. Those engineers made all kinds of studies before they bid on the project."

Lisa shifted in her chair. "You know Clint's been in Peru."

"Don't postpone it, Lisa. You'll throw your case right out the window, and your husband knows it."

She took a deep breath. It did sound foolish, now that she'd discussed it with someone else. Clint had seemed reasonable, yet she knew his powers of persuasion and she knew her own susceptibility to his wishes. She bit her lip. "Tom, I've promised. I've committed myself on this."

He shrugged. "So change your mind." He leaned closer, his voice intense. "You'd better, Lisa, or you've lost. If Callaway wanted facts, he could have gotten them, studied them tonight, and come up with an assessment of the problem by tomorrow." He regarded her intently. "You know he can influence you more than the average person can."

She blushed, but before she could answer, he continued. "Promise me this. Don't ask for the delay until the first of next week. You'll have time. Let me check into Callaway's company. I haven't done so before." He smiled disarmingly and leaned back in the chair. "Bad journalism! Rule number one is always get all the facts. The old man died a few months ago, and Callaway has a new president. The son is home from Peru. Let me find out a little more about them, will you?"

She considered his request. While she faced him in silence, he leaned forward and took her hand. "It can't hurt to wait a few days to ask for a postponement. I'm an impartial bystander, Lisa. I don't have anything invested in this. Don't do it. You'll kill your chance for success if you weaken now. Wait a few days, is all I ask. I hate to see you do this, because..." He paused and swore softly.

She tilted her head to regard him. "Because..." she prompted.

His dark-brown eyes were intent. "...Because I think your husband is working on your emotions," he finished. "If anyone else had made that request, you'd have thrown him out on his ear. You've already changed since the first time we talked. You're not as forceful when you discuss the lake."

She glanced down at the glittering solitaire on her finger. "Maybe you're right." She raised her head and faced him. "All right, Tom. I won't ask for the delay until next week. I'll have to do so by Tuesday."

"That's good enough," he replied. He looked around. "We'd better get out of here before everyone starts coming to work."

She glanced at the clock on his desk. "Good heavens!

I didn't realize it was so late." She rose, and together they went down to the car.

At the door of her apartment, Tom turned and looked at her. "It was fun, Lisa. You won't let that husband of yours talk you out of waiting until Tuesday, will you?"

Even though his tone was light, Lisa knew he was in earnest. She shook her head. "No, I promise. I had a good time tonight, Tom."

He smiled and drew her to him. His arms slid around her, and he leaned forward to kiss her.

Briefly, Lisa returned his kiss, then lightly pushed against his chest. She felt his hands fumbling with the buttons of her coat, then moving intimately over her body. He shifted, and whispered into her ear, "Where's your key?"

Lisa pushed against his chest once more. "Tom, you're going too fast. Please..."

Immediately he stepped away and gazed down at her. "You're gorgeous, Lisa."

"Now, Tom!" She smiled. "I'd better go in. Thank you for dinner."

The corner of his mouth lifted in a sardonic smile. "And you're sending me on my way." He touched her chin. "You ought to give someone else a chance." His hand slid around her waist again. "Come on, Lisa, relax. Clint Callaway isn't the only man in the world."

"No, Tom," she began to protest, but he pulled her close and leaned forward to kiss her once more. Lisa struggled, to little avail.

Finally he raised his head and gazed into her eyes. "Lisa..."

She stepped back and grasped his wrists to move his arms away. "Tom, I do have to go in."

He studied her a moment, then shrugged. "Okay—for now. I'll call you tomorrow." He waited until she'd entered the apartment; then he headed for his car. Lisa closed the door quietly and leaned against it.

She felt curiously drained. Gradually she explored the reason. She had responded to Tom's first kiss, but it had meant nothing. She squeezed her eyes shut. Clint. Always Clint. Would she ever forget? Ever get over him? She sighed and moved through the quiet apartment.

At the thought of Tom's hands on her, she rubbed her arms as if chilled. She could never be like Eileen, who went from man to man with enthusiasm.

The shrill ring of the phone startled her, and she reached for it quickly.

Clint's familiar baritone sent a flood of warmth coursing through her. "Hi. I've been trying to get you. Can you talk a minute?"

Lisa pulled the phone over to a chair and sat down. "Yes."

"I have to leave town Thursday and Friday. I thought I'd check our arrangements for driving to the Glass Mountains. What time would you like to leave?"

Lisa ran her finger over the phone. " Clint, I planned on an early start."

"Four o'clock?"

She laughed. "Not quite that early. I thought around six in the morning."

"Fine. I'll be by at six to pick you up. I haven't had a chance yet to look at the papers you gave me. I'm taking them to Denver with me. Lisa, before I left you at lunch, you said you had some additional information. I'd like to swing by the office in the morning and pick it up on my way to the airport."

"I won't be there if you come by before ten o'clock, Clint. I have an appointment. Eileen can give the folder to you. She knows where it is, and I'm sure she'd be delighted."

He laughed. "Fine. I'll see you Saturday morning, Lisa."

"Okay, Clint."

His voice dropped to that intimate huskiness she recalled so well. "Good night, honey."

"Good night, Clint." She replaced the receiver and sat in silence, with his words echoing in her ear. The mere sound of Clint's voice could stir her more than Tom Perkins's passionate kiss. She rose and went to bed. During the night she dreamed of Clint, of walking through deep snowbanks with him, then losing sight of him and peering through swirling snow to search for him. Calling for him, she was awakened by her own cry. Startled, she sat up and gazed around the darkened bedroom. She had cried Clint's name aloud! Perspiration beaded her forehead, and her palms felt clammy. She rose to get a drink of water, then returned to lie in the dark for a time before she drifted into a dreamless sleep.

chapter 8

FIRST THING THE next morning, Lisa called Eileen, who promised eagerly to deliver the information to Clint. When Lisa reached the office, she asked Nancy if Eileen had found the folder to give Clint. Nancy was certain she had, because Eileen had left with Clint. Lisa gazed at her in surprise, then moved on to her office and soon forgot about it while she worked.

Beneath a warm sun, Thursday and Friday passed rapidly. Friday night Lisa packed a picnic hamper and got ready for the excursion on Saturday. At six o'clock sharp, Clint appeared.

When Lisa swung open the door, Clint leaned against the jamb and smiled at her. His gray eyes were bold, roaming over her as if he could see beneath the jeans and blue blouse. She blushed and moved toward the kitchen.

He followed, and she glanced at him. His long legs were covered in blue denims, and he wore a thickly curled sheepskin jacket.

Clint took the hamper from her hands. "I'll carry this. I think we're in for good weather."

Lisa locked up and hurried to the car. As soon as they pulled away from the curb, she settled down in the seat and gazed out the window. Alternating with stretches of darkness, streetlamps shed wide circles of yellow light. They left the city limits and sped through the dark countryside. Lisa shifted in the seat and glanced out the back window at the graying sky in the east.

"Did you get in from Denver last night?" she asked.

"Yes. Lisa, I'm sorry, but I haven't had a chance yet to look at any of that information. We've sold some of our holdings in Denver and closed that branch; even my time on the plane was taken up with making final arrangements. I'll get to your folder tonight, I promise."

She nodded, and they rode in silence. Clint sped along the ribbon of road as it dipped in the gently rolling hills, then leveled out along flat plains bordered on either side by winter wheat. In the distance Lisa could see tall grain-elevators. Patches of snow lined bar ditches, but the day promised to be warm enough to melt the last traces completely.

Lisa shifted slightly to face Clint.

Engrossed in driving, his harsh features were turned away from her. His body was lean and powerful; the solid muscles of his long, hard legs showed against the tight denim. She felt an emptiness, a longing deep inside, then chided herself for being foolish. Nothing had changed, least of all Clint.

She must not be made vulnerable by his rugged male charm, because she would only be hurt again. He stretched his arm across the back of the seat and caressed her neck. He spoke quietly. "Tell me about the Glass Mountains."

She smiled at him. "After the Peruvian Andes, the Glass Mountains will seem like mere hills to you. Actually, they're mesas worn down by water and wind."

His fingers moved deftly, sending provocative tingles up her spine. It was growing increasingly difficult to keep her mind on the mountains. Her voice sounded far away and strained as she continued. "They contain selenite, a kind of gypsum. The selenite glitters in the sun and is supposed to be the reason for the name."

"I've worked northeast of here," Clint said, "and I'm familiar with gypsum in Oklahoma. It's mined here."

Was his voice growing more husky, she wondered,

or was it her imagination? His hands were warm, the skin calloused. She tried to think about what he was saying.

"As a matter of fact," he continued, "during the 1870s, U.S. Army detachments surveyed this state with gyp rock. They would measure the distance, drive a mile, and drop a rock to mark each section line."

She tilted her head to look at him. "I didn't know that, Clint. Can I use that in my article?"

He smiled. "Sure. Have you had breakfast?"

She shook her head. "I've had orange juice. I don't usually eat breakfast."

Another quick glance was directed her way. "Since when? As I recall, you liked breakfast more than any other meal." His voice was tender as he added, "I remember a great deal about you, Lisa. You'll never know how many hours I've thought of you."

She looked into his eyes. For a fleeting instant she was tempted to believe him. His wide gray eyes were piercing, appealing, with the thick fringe of black lashes. The harsh lines had softened. She noticed the crook in his nose.

Without thinking, she asked, "What happened to your nose?"

Momentarily, he appeared surprised, then rubbed his finger against tan flesh. "I broke it in a fight."

What kind of savage life had he led? she wondered. He certainly had come back changed from the person he was when he left. He was all muscle, brawn, and power, and deeply tanned. What had happened to him in Peru?

"Where did you live in Peru?"

"I stayed at the Cuzco Hotel part of the time. I was on a vicuna ranch. If you're interested in conservation, there's plenty to be concerned about in Peru."

She laughed. "I don't think I'll take that on. This has proven to be more than I expected."

"They're trying to protect vicuna, ocelots, and jaguars," he continued. "Also, the Peruvian government is attempting to develop the forest-covered area beyond the eastern slopes of the Andes. It's wild and primitive country, still inhabited in remote places by Jivaro headhunters."

She studied him as he talked. Clearly, she could visualize Clint in a jungle; he looked as if he would be at ease with a spear in his hand, moving among wild animals and primitive people.

He squeezed her shoulder. "I'd like you to see Machu Picchu. The misty crags are two thousand feet above the Urubamba River."

"The pictures looked beautiful, but I don't think that would be the place for me, Clint. I don't like heights."

His voice was soft. "Its wild beauty might make you forget your fears. Most difficulties aren't overcome without a struggle. You shouldn't shut yourself away from life, Lisa. I would be there to protect you."

She turned away so that he would not see the color rise in her cheeks. "I brought a thermos of coffee, Clint. Would you like a cup?"

"Sure," he answered. As she reached into the hamper in the back, he continued, "The Inca empire began in Cuzco valley, then spread along the Andes, until Pizarro, the Spanish conquistador, began to destroy them. Some of the Incas escaped the Spanish by hiding at Machu Picchu."

Lisa retrieved the tall yellow thermos and turned to sit down again. She unscrewed the plastic top of the bottle. "How did you get in a fight?"

He looked amused; one black eyebrow climbed wickedly. "Are you talking about the fight when my nose was broken?"

Surprised, she answered, "Yes. You mean there were others?"

With a rakish flash of white, even teeth, he grinned, then nodded toward the thermos. "Watch out, Lisa, or you'll pour scalding coffee over your lap."

Startled, she returned her attention to the coffee. Embarrassed by her foolishness, Lisa bent over the thermos, poured quickly, and secured the top.

Clint accepted a plastic mug and rested it against the steering wheel while he drove. A gray wisp of steam spiraled upward from the hot coffee.

He sipped his coffee, then said, "When I first went down there I got into a good many brawls. I was unhappy and ready for a fight at the drop of a hat. I wasn't in a good humor for a long time. After all, our marriage was in terrible shape. I wasn't content about working thousands of miles from home. I wasn't familiar with the people or their customs. I had more responsibility thrust on me than I'd ever had before—and I drank too heavily."

He paused to sip at the coffee, then lowered his cup. "I fought for no reason and every reason. On the particular occasion of breaking my nose, it was over a woman."

When Lisa looked at him, Clint gave her a mocking grin. She turned away in anger. How like him to brag about a conquest. She wished she never had asked the question.

He remained silent and she turned to look at the terrain. She could easily picture him with dark-haired, olive-skinned señoritas.

"Don't you have any more questions about the fight, Lisa?" Clint asked softly.

"No, Clint. You said it was over a woman; that's sufficient." She met his gaze. His eyes danced with amusement, which heightened her aggravation.

She handed him a plastic spoon to stir the coffee.

His fingers locked over hers, and she could not pull away. She looked up to meet his steady, amused gaze.

"I think you always jump to wrong conclusions, Lisa."

She tried to hold her anger in check. She did not care to hear about the love affairs he'd had while he was gone. "What 'wrong conclusions' have I 'jumped' to this time?" she snapped.

His voice was tinged with mocking amusement. "The fight involved a woman, but not in the way you must think. In the worst dive I've even been in, I insulted the cook. She spouted a stream of angry Spanish at me, too fast to understand, then came at me with a knife. I tried to get out without having to strike a woman, but when I did a small man jumped me. I discovered later that he was her husband. One of my friends came to my aid, and it turned into a free-for-all. I came away with a broken nose and some bruises."

He grinned at her, and Lisa could not resist smiling back. With Clint's powerful physique, it was easy to imagine him in a brawl. "What did you leave behind?" she asked.

He chuckled. "They needed to clean the place anyway. I'm afraid we left it a shambles."

He moved slightly and continued to relate tales of his Peruvian experiences, descriptions of barren desert along the coast, methods of transporting necessities by soft-eyed llamas, of *chullpas*—ancient burial towers.

"You should see a straw bridge we crossed, Lisa. Villagers rebuild it every year, but it dates back to the Incas. *Keshwa chaca,* as they call it, was just hand-spun rope across a gorge over fifty feet above the river."

For a moment she wondered what it would have been like to have gone with him to Peru. Instantly, she banished the thought. She forced her attention back to his descriptions of Peru, then turned to gaze at the countryside.

Far more quickly than she had expected, they reached their destination. The sun had climbed, and there was a dewy freshness in the air. Clint turned off the highway, along a narrow rutted road. Finally he braked and cut the motor.

Nearby was a mesa, red with gray flat caprock. Deep red arroyos cut gashes into rounded earth. Gusty wind whipped across dry mesquite with a soft whistling sound, catching Lisa's long blond hair and whipping strands free from the clip at the back of her neck.

She tilted her face into the wind and watched a hawk circle lazily above, its wide wings spread and still as air currents carried him higher.

There was a wildness to the open country that matched what she found in Clint. He gazed at the landscape with smoldering gray eyes.

"I see what you mean," he remarked. "I wouldn't call these mountains. This is lonely country."

"I've read that, before statehood, outlaws hid here," she said. "There was one, Zip Wyatt—or Dick Yeager, which was his real name—who hid loot in a cave. Years later someone found it."

"I'd think anything could remain hidden out here." He glanced down and lifted a booted foot caked with mud. "Maybe we didn't wait as long as we should have for the ground to dry."

"It doesn't wash out easily, either." She smiled at him. "That's the gyp—it's used to make plaster of Paris."

Her gaze drifted over the open land. "This is a good example of why we need conservation. Once this area was covered in timber. Pioneer settlers stripped it to use and sell."

"You'd never guess there had been forests here." He turned to reach into the car for his camera. "Try this one, Lisa. It's an excellent camera." He moved close to show her how to operate it. All the time he talked, Lisa was conscious of his closeness, of the occasional light brush of his fingers on hers. Finally she accepted the camera, gave him hers to carry, and walked away to begin snapping pictures.

"Come here," he called. "Let's climb one of those mesas." Clint took her hand and moved ahead. After a strenuous climb, they reached the top.

They spent the next two hours, climbing, sliding down, collecting rocks, and taking pictures. Finally Clint remarked, "I'm getting mighty hungry."

"We're a long way from the car."

"I'll go back and get the hamper," he offered. When he turned around, Lisa fell into step beside him.

"I'll go with you, Clint," she said lightly.

With a smile he took her hand, and they returned to the Ferrari. The sun had climbed, and Clint shed the sheepskin, while Lisa continued to wear her denim jacket. She looked around. "Where do you want to eat?"

He took her arm and pointed with his other hand. "See that mesa? It's the tallest one in this area. How about eating on top?"

She looked at him in dismay. "That's quite a climb! It'll be a challenge."

He grinned down at her. "That's what makes life interesting. Come on."

By the time they reached the top, Lisa was starved. Clint spread out a blanket, and she knelt to unpack the hamper. He sat down beside her to remove smoked-beef sandwiches and a bag of potato chips. She unwrapped slices of cheese and opened a jar of dill pickles. Suddenly she looked up to find Clint gazing at her intently.

With deliberation he reached across and unfastened the clip that held her hair. The silken strands swung loosely across her shoulders, and he smiled.

"That's the way I like your hair."

To force her thoughts to something impersonal, Lisa rummaged in the picnic hamper to unpack paper plates.

While they were eating, she looked around. "This area has a certain beauty to it. The sunshine on those rocks looks like diamonds sprinkled over the ground."

"It's beautiful and lonely," Clint observed. "You wouldn't think those dry creek beds would ever fill up with water."

"They recently found a skeleton of a wooly mammoth in one near here," she said.

They finished eating, and Lisa produced a tablet to write on, while Clint sat quietly nearby. With a low whine, the wind whipped around them. Clint gazed at the multicolored mesas, at the layers of earth streaked red, gray, and yellow.

"What are you writing about?" he asked.

She raised her head for a moment. "All this. The Department works closely with the Bureau of Tourism and Recreation. We're doing a series of brochures about scenic places, in order to attract tourists. State parks and recreation areas have more than seventy-five thousand acres of interesting scenery, with as much variety as you could possibly find, from granite mountains to areas like this. Oklahoma has more than a thousand square miles of water."

"Like Lake Tenkiller," he stated quietly.

Instantly she thought of the large stone lodge set in the cedar, pine, and oak trees of the Cookson Hills, where they had spent their honeymoon. Like closing a door at the sight of a forbidden object, she forced herself not to think beyond that.

With a lithe movement Clint stretched out on the blanket. He lay on his side, with his head propped up on his hand, and regarded her with smoldering eyes. His voice carried a velvety warmth. "It'll be spring again in just a few months. The dogwood will be in bloom. Do you remember, Lisa?"

She touched the tip of her tongue to dry lips, then realized what she was doing and closed her mouth quickly. "Clint, I need to finish this." She bent over the tablet.

His voice was husky. "Down in Peru I used to think about that time we had together. In my mind I would go over every moment of it. Remember how we could see the lake shimmer in the moonlight from the terrace of our room?"

Struggling to speak normally, Lisa kept her gaze fixed on the paper in her lap. "Little Sahara and its sand dunes are just north of here. Have you ever been there, Clint?"

"Nope. I remember the lake, the sweet, fresh smell of spring. I remember every inch of you stretched out on that big bed...."

She rose quickly and snapped the tablet shut. With her hands on her hips, she looked at him angrily. "You're impossible, Clint!"

His voice was a sensuous invitation. "Come here, Lisa."

"I wouldn't think of it, Clint. We'd better go."

With a quick movement he stood up. He shook the blanket and folded it neatly, then laid it on top of the hamper. Lisa started to walk away, but he caught her arm and turned her to face him. Wind whipped a long strand of yellow hair against his chest. She looked up at him questioningly.

"Whenever you drive through this part of the state you can see this mesa. It's tall enough to be visible for miles."

She glanced around, then returned her gaze to him.

"Every time you do," he continued, "I hope you look at it and remember this afternoon."

"Clint." She felt as winded as if she had just climbed the mesa. "You promised..."

Contradicting the message in his eyes, he said casually, "Let's call a momentary halt to promises, Lisa." His gray eyes darkened, and he pulled her into his arms. "This doesn't count," he murmured.

Her protests were effectively silenced. His lips were fiery, demanding, conveying pent-up desire he had so casually hidden all day.

Standing on the plateau, buffeted by a strong south wind that whipped her hair around her face and fluttered the hem of her jacket, Lisa felt even more buffeted by his passionate kiss. As relentless as a gust of wind, it tore at her heart and her defenses.

Finally he moved; his lips brushed her ear, and he whispered, "I never should have gone off and left such a lovely wife behind. But then, you were so cold and determined. Maybe I needed some time in the jungle, grappling with the elements and people, in order to get a better perspective on us."

"You have to stop, Clint." She pushed him a few inches away. "You promised to keep things impersonal."

Tense lines bracketed his mouth, and his eyes were troubled. He placed his hands on her shoulders. "It's a damn difficult promise to keep. Come on, we'll head home." He moved away, then looked around at her and offered his hand. She accepted it and walked beside him until they began their descent.

When Lisa sat down in the car, she saw her reflection in the mirror and laughed. Both cheeks were rosy with windburn; there was a smudge of red dirt on her forehead. She glanced down. "I may never get the mud out of these clothes."

Clint placed the hamper in the back, then slid in beside her. He put his hand on her shoulder and smiled. "Even with mud on your face, you're pretty. It adds a certain— uh—interest to your looks."

She laughed and fished in her pocket for a handkerchief.

"Let's go home," he suggested, "wash up, and go out for some steaks."

"Fine," she replied, and noticed a quick flash of satisfaction before he started the ignition.

chapter 9

AT THE OUTSKIRTS of the city, he whipped into a grocery parking lot and turned to face her. "How about letting me show you my culinary achievements?"

She ignored each little warning in her mind. Her careful reserve was crumbling quickly. With a nod of agreement, Lisa smothered caution. She stepped out and helped Clint with the shopping. When they reached her apartment, she turned to him.

"You might as well come in and cook here." She regarded him closely. "You look as if you've been in town all day. I must have stepped in every mud puddle out there. Come in, Clint. I'll take a shower, and we can eat here. You don't need to change or clean up."

He agreed and gathered the sacks of groceries to carry them in. In the kitchen Lisa turned to him. "If you'll wait until I wash and change, I'll do the cooking."

He shook his head. "None of that. I told you I wanted to show you my culinary achievements. Off with you, now."

She headed for her room. When she had finished showering, she dried her hair, then dressed in a white sweater and slacks. Barefoot, she strolled through the apartment. At the door of the kitchen she paused.

Clint was at the counter, cutting a tomato into a green salad. Black hair curled at the open neck of his plaid shirt. He had rolled the sleeves high, and they were taut over the bulge of his muscles. The wide, hand-tooled belt circled a narrow waist and flat stomach. He was familiar yet a stranger—powerful, sensual, extremely attractive. He turned to look at her.

The tension between them increased. He faced her steadily. She felt as if she were looking into the eyes of a tiger, unreadable, primitive.

She didn't know which was more unnerving—his calm assurance or his silent, hungry stare. She forced her voice to a lightness she didn't feel. "You seem to be remarkably domesticated."

From the counter he picked up two chilled glasses and extended one to her. "Here's a Peruvian drink for you— *pisco* sours made with grape brandy."

She accepted the drink, then paused as he raised his in a toast. "Here's to a happy future." Without so much as a blink in his piercing study of her, he clinked their glasses together.

Clint sipped, then lowered his glass. The gray of his eyes was like smoke, opaque, yet conveying a message as clearly as if he were speaking and as tangible as if his hand were on her, instead of merely his burning gaze.

"Maybe this was a mistake," she whispered.

"It's never a mistake for us to be together," he murmured in a honeyed tone that sent a ripple of excitement through her.

"You're breaking your promise again, Clint."

"I'm not touching you at all, Lisa. I'm keeping my word this time."

"You don't have to touch me, when you look at me like that."

His voice deepened. "Lisa, why don't you give us a chance? We've both changed, matured. I don't want a divorce."

"Nothing has really changed between us, Clint," she answered. Suddenly it was essential to get away from his compelling, devouring gaze. She brushed past him and opened the oven. "Dinner will burn if we aren't careful." She poked the potatoes with a fork.

"You're evading the issue."

She closed the oven and faced him. "No, I'm not. Have you changed, Clint? The decision will always be before us. Do I give up everything, my career, my opportunities, in order to go with you so you can pursue yours?"

"Lisa, when I had to go to Peru, I asked you then what you wanted me to do. Did you want me to quit and let you support me? Or go to work for my father's competitor?"

"You could have done something else at Callaway."

He shifted his weight. "It was Dad's company, and he gave me that assignment and said I had to take it or get out."

Her voice was tight, and she felt her nails bite into her hands. "I always thought he did it on purpose to..."

Clint frowned. "You never said that before, but since you told me about his offer, I'm beginning to see you might be right."

"Clint, your father lived in a very high style. You know I'm not the woman he had in mind for you to marry."

"I don't know, Lisa. There's your own family. At the time you felt you had to prove yourself. Even though they were all gone, you had that family to live up to. Now you've done all that. You've enjoyed rapid, impressive promotions. How much more do you have to prove?"

"Clint, you're not one to talk. You wield a great deal of power, and you'll never give it up."

His gray eyes bore into her. "Are you in love with Tom Perkins?"

"No! I told you before, Clint—"

Her sentence was cut short as he suddenly pulled her

out of the way and yanked open the broiler. Smoke curled upwards, and Clint fanned it away. He placed the steaks on the stove burners, and they looked at the darkened meat.

"So much for my culinary abilities," he stated.

"Oh, no, Clint." Lisa turned the steaks, then placed pats of yellow butter on each. "They're all right. You don't have to have it so rare to be good." She cut into one slightly. "See, they're fine. Let's get the potatoes and salad."

As if by tacit agreement, they dropped the discussion of their troubles during dinner. They finished eating and cleaned the kitchen. Lisa was putting away the tablecloth when the doorbell rang. She opened the door to face Eileen.

Standing in the subdued illumination of the outside light, Eileen tugged a fur parka close under her chin. "I was in the neighborhood, Lisa, and I thought I'd bring you this book on houseplants. You said you'd like to read it, and I keep forgetting to bring it to the office." She glanced past Lisa at Clint, who lounged in a doorway.

"Oh, I'm sorry. I didn't realize you had company."

"Hi," Clint remarked.

Lisa stepped to one side. "Come in, Eileen, and take off your coat."

"I hate to interrupt," Eileen answered, but she stepped inside and handed the parka to Lisa. "I'll just stay a minute, then go."

While Lisa hung the jacket in the closet, Clint asked Eileen if she'd like a drink. He mixed it, and Eileen sat down beside him.

Lisa crossed over to the fireplace and knelt down to lay a fire. She arranged kindling and papers, then held a match to them.

"You have a very capable wife," Eileen remarked. "I never could build a fire. I was a lousy Girl Scout."

She sipped the rum drink and asked, "Did you tell Lisa about my application?"

Lisa glanced questioningly at Clint. "No, I haven't," he said. His gaze met Lisa's. "Eileen has put in an application for a secretarial job at Callaway's."

Lisa straightened and looked at Eileen in surprise. "That is news! Have you resigned?"

Eileen patted Clint's knee. "No. That's up to your husband. I don't want to resign unless I get the job." She looked at Clint expectantly.

He leaned back on the sofa and stretched out his long legs. "Come by the office Monday, Eileen. How about ten o'clock? We can discuss it then."

"Fine. Did my aunt call you about Peru?"

Their conversation continued, while Lisa worked over the logs, but surprise still rocked her.

Why did Eileen want to change jobs and work at Callaway's? Had she sought the job to be near Clint? That didn't make sense, because he'd be leaving soon, going back to Peru. Lisa glanced over her shoulder and looked at them seated close together on the sofa.

Clint was relaxed, his long legs stretched out, listening to Eileen. She was turned toward him, her knees touching him as she talked animatedly about Peru. Her bright-blue ski pants and sweater fit like a second skin and contrasted with the mop of red curls that framed her face.

Lisa placed a log on the fire and watched the small tongue of orange curl around the wood. Why hadn't Clint mentioned Eileen's application?

The wood darkened as the flame dwindled. There were so many men in Eileen's life. There was no reason to be particularly drawn to Clint, but even as she had that thought, Lisa realized there were several reasons. Clint could interest Eileen because he was handsome in a rugged way, sensuous, wealthy. And soon he'd be single.

Jabbing at the logs, she concentrated on the fire until

it was blazing. She sat on the floor and listened to them talk of Peru—Eileen's questions and Clint's answers.

Lisa watched with amusement tinged with mild irritation as Eileen flirted openly with Clint. He remained pleasantly detached and seemingly unaware of the casual brush of leg against leg, of breast against his arm when Eileen moved to stub out her cigarette. Finally she rose and announced she had to leave.

As soon as Lisa closed the door behind Eileen, she turned and smiled at Clint. "Your charm is as magnetic as ever."

"I imagine her actions are as automatic as putting the car in gear," he said. "If I'd been a two-headed monster, I'd have received the same treatment."

"Hardly, Clint."

"I wish I could evoke that response from you, Lisa. You're the only one who counts."

She ran her finger along the back of a chair. "Why didn't you tell me she wants to work for you?"

He shrugged. "I forgot all about it." His eyes narrowed, and he looked at her intently. "What difference does it make?"

She picked up the book Eileen had left, and answered casually, "No reason. It just seemed natural for you to tell me."

He crossed the room toward her. Lisa watched him approach. He moved with the supple ease of a jungle cat. His black boots gleamed dully in the light. She turned quickly. "The fire is about to die." She reached for a log, but his hand was quicker.

"Here, let me do that."

She twisted away. "I can manage," she answered. In her haste, she dropped the log.

Clint scooped it up, then looked at her with a sardonic glint. "Did it ever occur to you, Lisa, that independence can be carried too far to be a virtue?"

She pushed her hair away from her face and rose.

"I think not," she retorted, "but then, we never did agree on anything." She stepped back as he placed more logs on the fire.

As he leaned over the hearth, his plaid shirt stretched tight across his broad shoulders, the hard muscles of his calves showed clearly against the narrow legs of his jeans. He straightened and faced her. "Oh, yes, we did agree on some things, or we wouldn't be married now."

They looked at each other a moment in silence. A cinder popped and a log dropped, sending sparks flying up the chimney, but neither noticed. Clint's gray eyes deepened to slate. He looked down at her, then his arm swept around her and tightened, pulling her against his lean, tough body. His head came down and his lips brushed hers before Lisa jerked her face to one side.

In a small voice, she gasped, "Clint, you're taking what you want and doing exactly as you please without any regard for my wishes!"

"You don't want this?" He caught her chin, turning her mouth up to his. His lips sought hers, exploring, kissing her hungrily.

She hated the uncontrollable feelings he could arouse so effortlessly in her. Inside, she felt as if she had suddenly plummeted off the edge of that mesa they had stood on only a few hours earlier. A wave of longing began in the pit of her stomach and burst up through her. Her head felt too heavy for her slender neck, her eyelids too weighted down to open.

He paused and looked down at her. With a sardonic gleam in his eyes, he locked strong fingers in silky strands of her golden hair.

"You feel the same thing I do," he whispered. "We were meant for each other, Lisa. Stop fighting me. Let me take care of you, love you as you should be loved."

She felt devastated by pent-up longing and desire. Just to look into his eyes and see those yearnings mirrored there sent tingles along her spine.

"Clint," she whispered, then she was crushed in his arms. His mouth sought hers, parting her lips with a frenzied eagerness.

His arm circled her narrow waist, while his free hand moved with deliberation. Aware of the burning touch of his legs, the length of his body pressing hers, Lisa struggled faintly.

She knew the strong, capable fingers that could so easily build and repair. Now, with all their deftness and agility, the same hands were at work rebuilding and creating a physical longing in her, stroking her smooth, firm flesh into a quivering need for him.

"Clint, don't do this," she murmured in one last gasping effort for sanity and reason.

His arms relexed. Their restraint was gone, as he barely held her. "Go on, Lisa. Walk away if you don't want me to make love to you," he whispered huskily into her ear. "Leave now . . ."

Her feet might as well have been imbedded in the floor. She couldn't move away. Her body was starved for his touch; quivering, she swayed toward him.

Unheeded, their clothing fell away. The air was cold on her bare flesh. She felt only his caresses, which were obscuring all thought, leaving a void filled by pure longing.

With the combination of precision and recklessness that had erected the steel bridge over the chasm in the Andean mountains, he proceeded to drown all her protests. His fingers traced their way down her spine and explored her long, silken legs.

Languorous warmth diffused through her limbs, to be gradually replaced by a mushrooming eagerness.

He lifted her effortlessly in his arms and placed her on the yellow sofa. As he crushed her against him, the buttons of his shirt bit into her flesh. It was difficult to utter a sound, but Lisa whispered, "Clint . . ."

He was gone, sitting up to fling away the plaid shirt

before lifting her in his arms again. His deep-coppery skin was dark against hers; black curls framed his face.

Bristles along his jaw scratched her lips as he turned his head. He leaned over her naked body and tilted her face up to his.

Placing his hands on the sides of her face, he said earnestly, "You're still my wife, Lisa. You'll see how much I need you . . . how much I love you . . ."

With her hands against his warm, bare chest, she could feel his heart thudding as violently as her own. She murmured against his throat, "This is senseless and unfair, Clint."

He pulled her close, molding her against his hard maleness. His hands drifted over her, arousing new sensations, new pleasures, constructing from feathery caresses a wild passion, building a physical bond that was stronger than all her cool logic.

With the tenderest of touches, his hands stripped away her reserve and demolished all her protests.

Lisa lost all sense of time and awareness of any anger she felt toward him. Moving against him, experiencing rapture she had not known was possible, she clung to his powerful body.

He paused above her; his gray eyes were filled with something undefinable. They raked over her pale, creamy skin.

He groaned aloud, bending down to scoop her up and kiss her passionately.

He cradled her in his arms; golden hair spilled over his bronze shoulder. He murmured against her throat, "How I've longed for you . . ."

The words were silenced by his mouth upon her warm flesh as he kissed her, moving his head lower across a ripe, firm breast. His thick black curls tickled her smooth skin.

Lisa's desire reached a feverish pitch. With a supple motion, she twisted against him.

He rose and stripped off his jeans. Lisa drew in a sharp breath at the sight of his virile body. Firelight cast dancing shadows over smooth, taut muscles. He had changed, grown tough and strong, yet she knew every inch of the satiny bronze skin. She reached up and uttered a small cry of longing.

His weight came down on her, and his mouth took hers. His knee shifted between her slender legs, and Lisa was lost in rapture that built like a tidal wave until it finally crashed in an explosion of ecstasy.

Awareness of the world around her began to return in bits and pieces. She shifted slightly to ease the pressure of his shoulder on her. She gloried in the loving possessiveness of his arms wrapped around her shoulders and waist.

With a lithe movement, Clint turned and lay beneath her. He smiled at her lovingly and pulled her close to kiss her with such tenderness that Lisa felt as if she would dissolve.

He rolled over to lay beside her and prop his head up on his hand to gaze down at her. His fingers smoothed the golden hair away from her face. His voice was husky as he said, "That's what I've wanted every single night, Lisa, since I left for Peru."

"Oh, Clint!" She tilted her lips up eagerly for his kiss. How could they have had such arguments!

He grasped a handful of her silky hair and brushed the ends across his cheek. "Your hair always smells good, Lisa. I used to dream about this golden hair." His eyes darkened. "I dreamed about every bit of you." He settled closer and pulled her into the crook of his arm, while he propped his head on his other arm, then closed his eyes. "This is heaven," he murmured.

She lay pressed against the length of his body, with one hand on his furred chest. She shifted slightly to gaze at him and saw that his eyes were closed. The long black lashes were feathered against his prominent cheekbones.

She touched his jaw lightly, and he opened his eyes, then smiled at her and kissed her temple.

Lisa's arms tightened around him, and she exhaled contentedly, then closed her eyes. The fire crackled and a log tumbled, sending sparks up the chimney.

It took two long rings of the doorbell before the sound penetrated her consciousness. Clint swore and whispered against her ear, "Ignore it, Lisa."

Lisa turned to him, lifting her lips to his, but the bell continued a demanding, incessant ringing until she sighed and pushed against his shoulders. "Let me go, Clint. It could be an emergency."

She rose to swiftly pull on her clothes. Behind her she could hear the rustle of Clint moving about. She glanced over her shoulder, and he was gone. Lisa hurried to the door and asked who was there.

Tom Perkins's voice carried clearly through the door. Suddenly Lisa felt a cloud of foreboding descend on her. She wanted to call to Tom to leave, yet she knew it was impossible.

Wearily she opened the door and faced him.

chapter 10

"LISA, I'M SORRY to barge in at this hour, but I had to wake you." Excitement filled his voice. "Look here: early editions of the Sunday paper are out. I couldn't wait to show you the write-up we got."

Lisa didn't want to invite him inside. Staring at Tom, she stood in the darkened entryway while cold blasts of wind whipped inside. She wanted him to disappear as quickly as possible, and she didn't want to see the article. Momentarily, she even wished she had never been involved in a project that opposed Clint's company.

Unbuttoning his brown topcoat, Tom stepped into the hall and closed the door. He turned around. "Here, Lisa, I brought copies. This will give you ammunition for your cause and against that husband of yours. You can't delay the hearing after this comes out. You'll be glad you agreed with me. Wait until Callaway reads it. . . ."

"Which will be quite soon," Clint drawled, coming up behind Lisa.

She glanced up at him. He looked calm and composed. Only the glacial gray in his eyes indicated otherwise.

With a sinking feeling, Lisa feared he had overheard all of Tom's remarks.

Looking at Clint, Tom's eyes narrowed. For an instant his gaze went back and forth between Clint and Lisa. A dark-red flush crept over his face; then he said, "I'm sorry, Lisa. I didn't realize you had company."

Tom's gaze went over her, taking in her appearance. Lisa blushed hotly. Whether she appeared rumpled or not, she felt as if her hasty pulling on of her clothes showed.

Tom's voice was cold. "I see I'm interrupting. I'll call you later, Lisa."

Wishing with all her heart that he would go, she said quietly, "I'll read the article, Tom." She stepped to the door as he left. He turned and took her wrist, then motioned to her with a jerk of his head.

"What is it?" Lisa asked, resisting his insistent tug, but Tom pulled on her wrist until she stepped outside. He reached around her and closed the door.

Lisa frowned. "Tom, please . . ."

"Lisa," he interrupted, "be careful he isn't just working on your emotions to sway your opinion about the lake."

Mild irritation rippled through her. "Tom, I do have to go in. Clint's waiting, and it's freezing."

He released the door handle and nodded. "Good night, Lisa. I'll call you tomorrow."

As much as she dreaded facing Clint, she stepped inside quickly and closed the door behind her. He was still standing in the hallway.

At the sight of him she wanted to fling aside the paper, throw her arms around his neck, and forget everything else. With a longing that tore at her, she wanted to obliterate from her mind all their differences, to exclude them with the hard, solid feel of Clint's body against hers. But the look in his eyes stopped her.

His gray eyes had deepened to slate; he returned her gaze coldly and reached for the Sunday paper, removing it from her icy fingers. He raised it to read.

Lisa moved beside him to study it. On the front sheet of the supplement was a large sketch of her, with a caption that read ENVIRONMENTALIST BATTLES CORPORATION.

Clint opened to the article. Peering over his arm, Lisa read hastily.

Pain curled inside as she scanned the damaging words. There was a picture of her seated behind her desk, pencil poised. Next to it, bold, dark print read ANGRY WIFE HAS EXECUTIVE HUSBAND ON GRILL . . .

"Clint, I didn't mean for it to sound like that. . . ."

No Arctic glacier could have been more silent, chilling, or unapproachable than Clint, yet at the same time Lisa knew she faced a volatile, pent-up fury that could explode at any moment.

Without a movement or word, his eyes and features conveyed an anger that terrified her. She wanted to be anywhere on earth except in her own hallway with Clint.

His voice was a demanding rasp. "Did you ask for a postponement of the hearing?" He added with quiet emphasis, each word bitten off, "As you said you would."

"I still can next week," she murmured. "Clint, I didn't intend for Tom to write an article that makes you or your company sound like a villain."

He made a harsh sound deep in his throat. "I find that a little difficult to accept, Lisa. You gave Perkins every word of that information." He jammed the paper into her hand and opened the hall closet to remove his jacket.

Shrugging his broad shoulders into the sheepskin, he growled, "Thanks for the day—it's been interesting."

She rushed over to him and placed her hand on his arm. She felt the rigid tenseness of muscle beneath his sleeve. "Clint, please listen—"

"I'll listen, all right! I'll listen to every word at that hearing. I thought I could count on you, Lisa, when you said you'd ask for a postponement."

"Clint, I still can . . ." She looked up at him.

He yanked his arm free and opened the door, then paused. "Lisa, you seem to know exactly what you want, but I've asked some questions and I'll warn you—watch out for Perkins. He's a woman chaser. You may not want to believe it, but he's fairly well known in certain circles." He shrugged slightly and added over her protest, "That's a fine article, with lots of publicity for you. It should do wonders for your career!"

He turned to the door and was gone in a flash. Lisa hurried after him, but he was already striding down the walk toward his car.

She stared at his straight back and knew it was useless to speak to him again. She watched him climb into the car, then drive away. As soon as the red taillights disappeared around the corner, she closed the door.

She moved woodenly, to sink down on the sofa. Idly, Lisa ran her fingers over a cushion still wrinkled from Clint's weight. Hot tears stung her eyes and ran down her cheeks.

She thought of the interlude before Tom's appearance. Longing filled her at the memory of Clint's lovemaking. She remembered each caress, each kiss, and a wild thrill coursed through her. She thought of them together afterwards, of the warm, cherished feeling of being in his arms.

For months she had expected their separation to end in divorce. In spite of their early love, circumstances seemed unalterable, Clint implacable in his stand. All the time they had been apart, she had expected eventually to seek a divorce. But tonight that conviction had been shaken.

For the first time in their stormy relationship since the rift, she realized she was fully, irrevocably in love with Clint.

Equally sure was the realization that she had driven him away. Unless she dropped her campaign to save the lake, she could never breach their differences now. The article was too damaging to be discounted with a mild apology.

Thinking of Clint's stormy, passionate love, she gazed

into the dying embers of the fire, quivering with need for him.

Now that she had faced the fact that she loved him, her desire for him grew. She realized how strongly she had fought against it all this time, allowing hurts and injured emotions to reign, afraid to love, afraid to be vulnerable or depend on him. Now she wanted another chance.

Lisa twisted to place her head on a cushion and let the tears flow, unheeded.

Finally she grew quiet, then rose and got ready for bed. When she reached into the closet for a gown, she paused, then stood on tiptoe. From the corner of a high shelf she retrieved a picture wrapped in tissue paper. She pushed away the paper to look at her wedding picture.

Younger and thinner, Clint stood beside her, smiling at the camera. She ran her fingers lightly over the smooth glass and remembered when they had first met. She had been a senior in college, and Clint had returned to get a master's degree in engineering. A mutual friend had introduced them, and Clint had asked her to a football game. They dated all fall, and by winter they were engaged. They were married early in the spring and had over a year together before circumstances altered their lives.

Lisa sighed and rewrapped the picture carefully, then returned it to the shelf.

After brushing her hair until it crackled, she retrieved the hateful paper, turned down cool sheets, and climbed into bed to read the article.

Word upon word built a case of damaging accusations against Clint's company. The article described a young woman single-handedly challenging grasping mercenaries who were intent on demolishing wildlife.

In the solitude and silence of her own room, Lisa shook her head and whispered, "No . . ."

Each word was like a brick, one after another joining

to build a wall to separate her from Clint. Agony filled Lisa.

Suddenly she stiffened with shock, her gaze riveted to the page.

Sitting as quietly as if she had been stunned by a deluge of ice water, Lisa read the headline for the second column of the article. CLINT CALLAWAY, PRESIDENT OF CALLAWAY AND ASSOCIATES.

Somehow she had missed the paragraph earlier. She smoothed the paper across her lap and looked at it again. Her face flushed, and she raised her head to gaze into space. Clint was president of Callaway. . . .

A sharp pain shot through her middle. She clenched her fists into tight balls and put them against her eyes, hating the hot tears that stung her.

Once more she had opened her heart to Clint, had been charmed by him, swept off her feet—only to be hurt. Never, ever, had he told her that he, not Charles Mallory, was now president of the company.

She glanced at the phone, then picked up the receiver and asked information for Clint's number.

Numbly, she listened to the phone ringing. Finally there was a click, and Clint growled hello into the phone.

She looked down at the newspaper. The headline seemed to leap at her.

"Clint, this is Lisa." She paused. "Are you president of Callaway?"

She knew the answer before he said it, yet it still hurt. "Yes."

"Why didn't you tell me?"

His voice still carried strains of anger. His words were clipped. "I started to, then each time something inter- rupted me."

She closed her eyes, making no attempt to wipe away the hot tears that coursed down her cheeks.

Her tone was flat as she said, "You're not returning to Peru."

"No."

"All this time, then, you knew you'd live here—that the barrier between us was gone, yet you let me go on thinking—"

He became even more gruff as he interrupted. "After reading that article, I can't see that it makes any difference. Lisa, you told me you'd postpone the hearing. You said you weren't doing this out of spite, yet you didn't ask for a delay, and that story was as spiteful as possible!"

Hot anger mingled with the pain she suffered. "I didn't write it."

"I know; Perkins did. He made it far more emotional than was necessary."

"That's ridiculous!" Wrath kindled in Lisa and spilled over. "At least he was honest. Did the board of directors send you here to win me over?"

There was a moment of silence; then his voice said, "Perkins could be using you just to further himself."

"So what if he is? Is there anything wrong with that?" she asked defensively. "Is that any worse than what you've been doing?"

"Lisa, my board of directors has nothing to do with my feelings for you! That's ridiculous. . . ."

"Did they ask you to get me to drop this?" When there was a pause, she insisted, "Did they, Clint?"

"Yes, but that—"

"Did they want you to see me about it?"

"Yes. Lisa, will you listen—"

"I think, Clint, I've listened far too much to you." Fury, resentment, and pain mushroomed inside her. "I'll call my lawyer Monday about a divorce."

At last the anger seemed to have drained out of his voice. "That's what you've had in mind all the time, isn't it?" he asked quietly.

"I don't know," she replied.

"That isn't what I want, Lisa."

"Isn't it?" Her pain was acute. She felt all her control

slipping away. "You could have resolved all our differences immediately if you'd told me you weren't returning to Peru. Why didn't you?" She rushed on, the words tumbling out of her mouth in an angry flow.

"Were you following the orders of your board of directors? You're hiring Eileen, Clint. I'm sure she's more than willing to cater to your arrogant whims!"

He swore, then commanded, "Lisa, listen—"

"Did the board vote for seduction, Clint? Did you think if you seduced me I'd drop the fight?"

"Lisa, dammit!" he exploded.

She slammed down the receiver. A sob burst from her throat, and she put her head in her hands and shook with sobs.

"Clint..." she whispered.

The jarring ring of the phone startled her. She pushed her hair away from her face and looked down at it. How easily she could visualize Clint's frown as he waited for her to answer.

She jumped up and moved away. The ringing continued, insistent and steady, until she yanked a pillow from the bed and thrust it over the phone.

For over an hour the phone continued to ring off and on, each sound a muffled hum. Finally it was silent. Sleep seemed hopeless, so Lisa got out paint and worked on the apartment until the early hours of the morning, when finally she was sufficiently exhausted to fall asleep.

chapter 11

WHEN LISA ARRIVED at work on Monday, Eileen was absent—probably at her interview with Clint, Lisa decided. She bit her lip at the thought that Eileen would be more than willing to soothe his anger.

Closing the door to the office, she sat down at her desk and gazed at the phone. All weekend since the call to Clint, she had mulled over getting a divorce. When her anger had cooled, only pain was left. Lisa was convinced Clint didn't want her back; he had taken her out simply to weaken her fight against his company. If he'd really wanted her to come back to him, all he'd had to do was return and tell her he wouldn't go back to Peru.

All the time Clint had been in South America, she had never called a lawyer. She knew now it was because, deep inside, she didn't want a divorce. She loved Clint.

Twice now, she had let him hurt her, but she couldn't stop longing for and loving him.

When they'd gotten married they had vowed to love each other for better or worse. She knew now that she did. Clint would have to ask for a divorce. She couldn't.

Suddenly afraid she would burst into tears in the office, she plunged into work in an effort to keep her personal problems out of her thoughts.

All morning she kept catching herself staring into space or reading the same line twice and still not understanding what she read. Without provocation, her thoughts drifted to Clint.

After studying information about the Alabaster Caverns, in northwestern Oklahoma, she decided it would be a good time to go. She made arrangements to take off Thursday.

To her chagrin and dismay, a councilman called to inform her that the hearing concerning the proposed highway had been postponed for two weeks. For a moment she wondered if Clint would think she had asked for the delay. Then she realized he'd make inquiries until he knew she'd had no part in the decision.

In the afternoon Tom called to say he had scheduled her for a brief interview on a local television news show on Tuesday evening.

Even as she agreed to the interview, she wondered if Clint would see it and become even angrier with her. She drew circles on a scrap of paper and said, "Tom, the article did give me a lot of publicity, but you twisted things a little."

He laughed. "Literary license! It stirred up support. We've had calls all morning about it."

"There have been some here, too," she said cautiously.

"Great! That's just what we wanted. I'm doing an article now to let people know about the hearing."

"Hold off on that, Tom."

There was silence a moment, then he said, "Hey, you're angry with me about that article, aren't you?"

"It was stronger than I expected. I appreciate what you've done, but I don't want any more publicity right now, Tom. I'll do the interview, but that's all."

His voice grew more subdued. "Lisa, what about the awards banquet? You'll get an award, and I want to cover it in the paper."

She'd forgotten about the banquet. "That's different."

"Let me take you to lunch today."

She declined. "Thank you anyway, but I'm going to Alabaster Caverns Thursday and I need to catch up on work."

His tone was eager once again. "I've never seen them, and I'd like pictures of them. May I join you?"

Lisa was at a loss as to how to refuse politely, yet she wanted the time alone.

"I promise I won't be any trouble," Tom added.

She laughed and relented. "Come on, then, but I'll warn you now, I plan on leaving around six in the morning."

"That's fine. I've always wondered what sunrise looks like. Now I'll get to see firsthand."

She laughed again. After a few more minutes' conversation, Lisa told Tom goodbye and went back to work.

The next day passed quickly, and the interview went well. Afterwards, Tom took her to dinner, then straight home, because she had more work to do.

Lisa noticed that Eileen was away from the office the first three days of the week. She speculated that Eileen had gotten the job at Callaway's and would not be back, but no one mentioned it. Finally, Nancy said Eileen had called in and asked for another day for personal matters. No one at the office knew any more about it than Lisa.

Wednesday night the phone rang, waking Lisa from a deep sleep. Tom's words rushed out. "Lisa, the entire main street of Macon, Oklahoma, is on fire. I've been asked to cover the story. Would you like to come with me instead of going to Alabaster Caverns?"

"I'm sorry about the fire," Lisa answered sleepily, "but I'd better go to the cave. At this time of the year they usually don't have tours. I've made special arrangements with the guide."

"I hate to see you drive up there alone," Tom said. "The weather prediction for the next few days isn't good."

"I'll be careful. I'd like to get my story."

"I can go tomorrow," he persisted.

"I'll be all right," Lisa answered. "Go on to the fire. I imagine you'll be in far more danger than I could possibly be. I won't get lost in the caverns, I promise."

He laughed. "I give up. Okay. I'll call you tonight."

Lisa told him goodbye and went back to sleep until the alarm woke her at dawn. Within an hour she was dressed in a navy-blue sweater and slacks, had eaten breakfast, and was on the road. It was a pleasant drive; the temperature had dropped, and a strong wind was coming down across the plains when she reached open land.

When she passed the Glass Mountains, it was impossible to resist looking at the high, flat mesa where she had picnicked with Clint.

With a stab of longing she recalled with total clarity every detail about the moment—the faint trace of smoke on his breath; the fine cotton of his plaid shirt; his warm hands and hard, lean body; the wind whipping against them with a hollow, sighing sound; and, most clearly of all, his demanding, warm lips that both satisfied and at the same time drove her to greater hungers.

Lisa was startled by a small cry and realized it was her own voice. "Clint . . ." she whispered. "I do need you . . ."

Lisa clutched the steering wheel and stared at the gray ribbon of road that stretched ahead between glittering mesas. In the cold January air sunlight reflected in sparkling dots of selenite.

No matter how much Clint had hurt her, even if he didn't want her back, Lisa acknowledged her love for him. She had walked out on him when he insisted on going to Peru. Now, with all her heart, she wished she hadn't done so.

Perhaps it wasn't too late. She pulled the car off to the shoulder of the road and frowned into space.

She was tempted to turn around and drive back to the

city immediately. Finally she gave herself a small shake and put the car in gear to continue on to Alabaster Caverns. It would be ridiculous to return home. She'd be back by evening and could call Clint then. If they got together and talked things over, perhaps there was still hope. She wondered if he still felt any love for her at all or if all he'd done and said was for the benefit of his company.

The Clint Callaway she had dated and married would never have done such a thing, but the man who returned from Peru was completely different, and she was uncertain about his thoughts or feelings.

She longed to hear his quick, easy laugh, to see the sparkle in his gray eyes when he was amused. With a sigh, Lisa turned on the radio and attempted to set her thoughts on the day ahead.

The midmorning weather report predicted a fifty percent chance of snow. Scanning the horizon, she saw only a dismal, cloud-filled sky. She'd be returning within the next few hours; an imminent storm seemed a remote possibility.

At last Lisa arrived at the small frame house of Mr. and Mrs. Lawick, who ran the small curio shop and served as guides to the cave.

Petite, with thick auburn hair, Mrs. Lawick put on a coat to accompany Lisa on the tour. On the phone she had warned Lisa to wear warm clothing, since the temperature in the cave was a year-round fifty-six degrees.

Switching on artificial lights as they strolled through the world's largest known gypsum cave, Mrs. Lawick paused whenever Lisa wanted to stop for pictures.

To catch the lustrous beauty of translucent alabaster, Lisa took a picture eighty feet below ground at the entrance. Then deep in the cave they stopped again as she snapped tiny bats hanging upside down, suspended from the ceiling. Their dark wings were folded like leaves around their dormant bodies, waiting like plants for warm spring weather. Three species of bats inhabited the cave—Cave Myotis, the Western Big-Eared bat, and, in summer, the Mexican Freetail.

She continued to snap pictures along the twenty-three-hundred-foot-long visitors' trail through Gun Barrel Tunnel, the Encampment Room, and at the underground lake. When they emerged from the upward-sloping path into open air, the world was covered in a thin dusting of snow.

Tiny flakes swirled and fell with wet coldness against Lisa's cheeks. Hastily, she thanked the Lawicks for the tour and declined to stay for coffee and cake, because she was anxious to start home.

She turned down the deserted asphalt road. The drifting snow would have looked beautiful if she didn't face several hours' drive through it.

Lisa switched on the radio for a weather report and discovered that a blizzard had moved rapidly into the northwestern part of the state, changing to rain in the central part. She could expect to drive out of the snow in little more than an hour's time.

She considered her choices. Once she left Mooreland, she'd have a long drive in open country, with no towns for refuge. Snow was being blown clear of the highway by wind that howled and shook the small car in violent gusts. Lisa reached Mooreland with so little difficulty that she decided to chance getting home.

Once in town, it was easy to see, but as soon as she passed the last small house and drove into open prairie, the world became white. For long stretches the highway was all but hidden.

She glanced at the sack lunch and thermos on the seat beside her, glad she hadn't touched them during the morning. She sighed and hunched over the wheel, straining to follow the strip of paving.

Within a quarter of an hour, the flakes grew denser. The wind rose, blowing snow in blinding gusts against the car. Lisa's speed dropped to twenty miles an hour, and she had to fight down rising panic.

She regretted her decision to continue home, but it was too late to turn back. She was well aware that this corner of the state was subject to more blizzards than just a county to the south, but she hadn't expected conditions to become so bad so fast.

The snow changed to sleet, which pinged against the hard metal. Sharp pebbles of ice bounced off the car. The Honda slid on a patch of ice, but Lisa regained control.

After a stretch of clear pavement, she encountered a deep drift that was difficult to drive through. Finally she hit a larger drift, the car slid, and she felt a slight drop as it skidded off the pavement onto a soft shoulder.

In vain Lisa tried to get free, but the tires spun, digging in deeper. Her apprehension rose, and she had to fight down a wave of hysteria. Her head in her hands, she tried to think rationally about her predicament. Snow usually didn't last long in Oklahoma; it could easily be gone by the next morning.

But thoughts of the next morning brought back her panic in full. To spend the night alone, stranded miles from anyone or any town, was a frightening prospect. She began to take stock of what was available. The gas gauge indicated the tank was three-fourths full, for which she was thankful. And she was relieved to have lunch and the thermos of hot coffee.

To conserve gas, she turned off the motor. As if some giant, unseen hand were rocking it, wind whipped against the car, shaking the vehicle. Lisa dozed. When she awoke, the air felt freezing. She restarted the motor until warmth from the heater began to penetrate the car.

She ate half the lunch, then folded away the remaining portion. Each time she ran the motor, she cracked the window down a fraction to let in fresh air, then closed it tightly when she turned off the ignition.

During the night she awoke to utter silence and knew the storm was over. By early morning she was exhausted from brief intervals of sleep, freezing cold, and the strain of the long hours.

She opened the door, stepped into a deep drift, and cleared off the windows, then climbed inside again to warm up. Ahead, the road was hidden by a huge drift, yet in the distance she spotted a stretch of gray paving where wind had blown the asphalt clean.

News on the radio stated that many motorists had been caught by the storm, stranded along several highways just as she had been. The temperature was expected to rise to fifty degrees, but Lisa knew it would take more than that to melt the high drift surrounding her car, much less to aid her in driving off the shoulder and onto the road.

The gas tank was nearly empty; another night in the car would be disastrous. With each passing hour, Lisa's anxiety increased. Once, during midday, she clambered onto the roof of the car to scan the horizon in all directions for a farmhouse, barn—any sign of life—but she saw nothing but an oil well pumping in the distance.

Later, she was finishing the last of the sandwich when she heard the motor of an approaching car. As it neared, she realized it wasn't a car, but a small plane. Immediately she thought of the snow-covered top of her car; she climbed out to sweep the remaining snow off the roof as rapidly as possible.

The bright red-and-white plane circled and flew low. Knowing it was useless to expect much from someone in a plane, Lisa waved wildly.

In return a wing waggled, and she felt a surge of hope, then watched the plane disappear from sight, toward the south.

Wearily she climbed back into the car, brushed snow from her wet slacks, and huddled in her seat for warmth. She dozed, then woke shivering, and turned on the ignition to use the last gasoline. A movement ahead caught her attention; squinting into the distance, she saw a large yellow road grader bearing ponderously down the road in her direction.

She leaned forward and strained to see, watching with mounting excitement and relief as it drew nearer. While the motor chugged noisily and sent dark plumes of diesel smoke spiraling into the sky, a heavy blade pushed the snow away.

Lisa's heart pounded with joy. Rescue! She jumped from the car as the machine neared. The driver shifted the throttle and slowed down.

Afraid he might drive on past and leave her, Lisa raced toward him. He stopped, rose from the seat, and reached down to pull her up.

"Thank goodness you're here!" she cried. "I'm so glad to see someone!"

"Even me?" a sardonic voice asked.

chapter 12

LISA HAD GIVEN him her hand and reached one foot on the step to climb up beside him. At his voice, she stopped and looked up in amazement to see Clint's face beneath the furry parka.

"You damn little fool!" he snapped. "Always trying to do the impossible by yourself." He yanked her up beside him in a quick movement that sent a wave of pain down her arm.

She could think of nothing to say except to ask, "How did you know I was here?"

"Tom Perkins has been searching for you. He called," he answered abruptly, then asked, "Where are the car keys?"

In her haste, she had left them in the ignition. She started to climb down. "The keys are in the car."

He grasped her arm. "Sit down," he commanded. "I'll get them."

She sank gratefully down in the warm cab and watched as he dropped lightly into the snow and crossed to the car in long strides. His suede, fur-lined parka, jeans, and black boots were vivid against the whiteness. He retrieved her keys, locked the car, and returned.

The door clanked shut, and Clint eased the throttle forward. They began to move in a rough, lumbering ride with a motor that drowned out all possibility of conversation. Clint turned the vehicle around and headed in the direction from which he'd come.

Within fifteen minutes the snow began to thin. In half an hour, it disappeared altogether. They entered Seiling and drove to a point near the railroad tracks where several large yellow road machines were parked.

Lisa studied Clint's profile, his bronze skin framed by thick black curls, and became aware of her own disheveled appearance. In her haste to reach the highway she had left her purse behind. She had no make-up, no comb, and her slacks were still damp below the knees from walking in the snow.

Clint cut the motor, jumped down, then reached up and swung her easily to the ground.

"How did you find me?" she asked.

"Perkins was worried. He called, looking for you." He took her arm as he talked, and crossed a gravel lot to a small wooden building, unlocked the padlock, placed the key to the road machine inside, then locked the door once again.

She looked up at him. "Does that equipment belong to the Callaway company?"

"No, but I have access to it," he answered tersely, and steered her toward a nearby cafe. "Lisa, what the hell were you trying to prove by driving into that storm?"

"I wasn't trying to prove anything," she replied defensively. "The storm wasn't bad when I left Mooreland; then it was too late to turn back."

Beneath a bright sun, the wide main street of town stretched ahead of them. Puddles of melted snow dotted the sidewalks and street. They approached steps to a boardwalk in front of the cafe. "I left Eileen here to wait for us. I thought you might want something to eat before we start home."

Lisa looked at him in surprise. "You brought Eileen with you?"

He glanced down. In a voice filled with stinging coldness, he replied, "I thought you'd rather not be alone with me." His eyes narrowed, and he searched her face. "That doesn't meet with your approval?"

The biting tone of his voice caused her to counter, "Would it matter if it didn't?"

Immediately she regretted her words. He turned and walked ahead, his long strides indicating his anger. Lisa reached out and caught his arm. "Clint, thank you for coming to get me."

The parka had fallen away from his face; his forehead was tan above a pair of pale sunglasses. Before he could reply, a voice cried, "Lisa!"

She turned and saw Eileen standing outside the door of the cafe, waving at them. Eileen had never looked more beautiful. Gone were the tight red curls. Instead soft waves framed her face and caught the sunlight, making her hair appear a burnished halo around her head. Her make-up was flawless, setting off her deep-green eyes. Her white fur parka was thrown open, revealing a skin-tight emerald-green sweater and stretch slacks that seemed molded to her lush, full figure.

Eileen's meticulous appearance made Lisa all the more aware of her own bedraggled one. Eileen hurried to meet them, and Clint turned toward her.

With bitter disappointment curling inside her, Lisa walked beside him. She had hoped to ride home alone with Clint, to have an opportunity to talk to him. Instead, with Eileen along, there would be no chance for a personal discussion.

Eileen rushed up and squeezed her hand. "You poor thing! You had us all worried to pieces." She looked up at Clint. "Was it the car we saw this morning?"

"Yes," he answered, and held the door open for them as they stepped inside the welcome warmth of the small cafe. Clint's boots clacked against a bare hardwood floor as they crossed to a table draped with a red-checkered tablecloth.

Lisa excused herself to hurry to the ladies' room. One glance in the mirror confirmed her suspicions. Her hair was in a tangle, her face smudged. Clint had found her at her worst.

She did what she could to repair the damage, then rejoined them. Clint was in a hurry to get back to Oklahoma City and had ordered sandwiches and drinks to go. He said he'd get the car and pick up Eileen and Lisa at the door.

On the ride home, Lisa climbed into the back seat of the mud-streaked black Ferrari and rode in silence, listening to Eileen's animated conversation. The redhead had slipped out of her parka and rode facing Clint, glancing over the seat at Lisa while she talked.

"How was the trip to the cave?" Eileen asked.

"It was beautiful," Lisa remarked. The visit to Alabaster Caverns seemed long ago, much longer than a mere twenty-four hours.

Lisa relaxed against the car seat. "The colors inside the cave are beautiful. The translucent stone looks pink and white and golden."

"Alabaster goes back to ancient civilizations, to biblical times and Egypt," Clint remarked. He met Lisa's gaze in the rearview mirror. She licked dry lips, wanting to cry aloud, *"Why didn't you come alone?"* She tried to pay attention to what he was saying.

He continued talking about alabaster. "In the pyramids they've found alabaster bowls and jars. There are two kinds of alabaster: Oriental, which is hard—it's marble—and gypsum."

Lisa gazed at him in surprise. "How did you know all that, Clint?"

He shrugged. "From working on highways and being familiar with gypsum in Oklahoma."

"Clint is a walking information center," Eileen added.

He glanced at her with wry amusement. "Are you saying I talk too much?" She protested, then he glanced in the rearview mirror to look at Lisa again. "In all the time I've traveled around this state, I've never been to that cave."

"It was snowing when I came out, so I didn't get to Cedar Canyon or anything nearby," Lisa said. "We need information on several places there—the Wildlife Refuge, Boiling Springs State Park, and Little Sahara."

"Does that mean you have to go back right away?" Clint asked harshly.

"No. I'll make certain about the weather next time," she assured him, embarrassed by the trouble she'd caused.

Eileen twisted to face her. "I guess this will bring you more publicity. Tom wanted to come along to take pictures and everything."

"Oh, surely not!" That was the last thing Lisa wanted.

"Really, he did," Eileen stated firmly. "He knows a good story when he sees one. He'll probably be waiting when we take you home."

"Well, there won't be any pictures or story," Lisa stated wearily, her spirits sinking even lower.

If Tom appeared with a camera after her ordeal, it would simply prove that Clint had been right about him. She couldn't imagine his being so insensitive as to want to take pictures, yet at the same time she realized he was a journalist. Any motorist stranded overnight during the storm would be a story.

Lisa wished Eileen would stop talking, her innocent voice causing ever-widening rifts between Clint and her. Perhaps the rifts were irreparably wide already and Eileen was doing nothing to change his feelings.

Eileen reached up and brushed an imaginary speck from the back of Clint's jacket. Her hand moved against his neck in swift, light touches.

With an unbearable ache, Lisa shifted and stared out the window at the gently rolling countryside. The sun was setting, its rays splayed against the winter sky. In the distance the ground was a gray blur blending with darkening clouds.

Eileen shifted toward Lisa. "I talked to Tom. He's worried sick about you. He said he asked you not to go, that he heard the weather would be bad."

Lisa wanted to reach across the seat and shake Eileen for talking continually about Tom as if that were where Lisa's only interest lay. Keeping the rising aggravation out of her voice, she answered calmly, "Eileen, you know how many times the weather report is wrong. Our weather can change in a flash."

Eileen looked at Clint. "I hope you realize how much trouble Clint has gone to for you."

Briefly, he glanced at Eileen and smiled, then faced the road. Again his eyes met Lisa's in the mirror.

She turned away quickly from the anger she saw reflected in their smoky depths. "I thanked Clint, Eileen. I'm extremely grateful to him."

Once again she caught his inscrutable stare, his gaze resting steadily on her. Her heart thumped heavily, and she wished he didn't have such power to stir her by a mere glance.

Eileen wiggled closer to the edge of her seat, leaning nearer to Clint, her full breasts pressed against his shoulder.

As if irresistibly drawn, Lisa glanced again in the rearview mirror and caught Clint's smoldering gaze. His eyes returned to the road. Lisa scooted to the right in the seat, out of his view.

Eileen shifted, but the widely spaced seats gave Lisa a clear view of her hand stretching across to rest on Clint's knee. Lisa saw his arm move slightly and guessed that he had covered Eileen's hand with his own.

She felt a stab of jealousy and wanted to cry out, to tell Eileen to take her hands off him, that he was her husband and not Eileen's property to touch. But it was impossible.

The thought of his wide, strong hand closed over Eileen's small white fingers sparked a deep longing in Lisa. She chided herself for being such a fool as not to have realized sooner how much she still loved him.

It was too late now, but still she intended to tell him, to let him know she was in love with him, whether he wanted her or not—and it was becoming painfully evident that he did not.

Eileen twisted to face her. "Remember the awards banquet the Department is having?"

In the tumultuous last two weeks, Lisa had not thought of the banquet. "I'd forgotten all about it, Eileen," she admitted.

"Well, I'm trying to get Clint to go with me, because Tom told me you'd asked him."

A surge of anger and dismay flashed through Lisa. "We discussed it when I first met Tom," she answered stiffly. "He asked if he could go."

Clint darted a questioning look at Lisa. Her words had been spoken so stiffly that even Eileen could not ignore them. She studied both of them as she replied, "I didn't mean to step in where I shouldn't—"

"Never mind, Eileen," Lisa interrupted. She felt tears of frustration well up, and turned to look out the window. Everything was going wrong. She remembered Eileen's words, "... *anything goes, where men are concerned. It's every woman for herself...*"

It was obvious Eileen had meant it. She wanted Clint and was not hiding the fact. Clint's voice interrupted her thoughts.

He looked over his shoulder at her. "Lisa, are you all right?"

She blinked and turned to smile at him. Raising her chin, she replied firmly, "I'm fine."

After another quick glance he faced the road again. Lisa watched as Clint withdrew a cigarette; Eileen leaned forward to light it for him. His rugged profile was toward

Lisa; he squinted against the smoke, with the corner of his mouth lifted in a brief smile of wry amusement.

Lisa thought of how she had fought with him, causing him difficulty after difficulty. Eileen hung on every word he uttered, smiling up at him, touching him lightly. It was no wonder he found her appealing.

When they finally turned the corner to her apartment, Lisa found it difficult to hide her disappointment and frustration at the sight of Tom's familiar blue car parked at the curb.

"See, there's Tom, just like I told you," Eileen said cheerily. "I'll tell him you don't want any pictures yet. I know you don't when you look like that."

Lisa waved a hand at Eileen; her frustration changed to anger. "That's all right, Eileen," she answered evenly. "I'll manage Tom. Clint, would you please drive to the back? It will give me a minute before I talk to Tom."

Without a word he did as she asked. Eileen turned to stare at her, her lower lip curled petulantly. "That's not very nice to Tom, Lisa. He'll see us drive right past."

Not trusting herself to speak, Lisa merely smiled and stared out the window. Eileen's gaze went over her. "Where's your purse, Lisa?"

"I left it in my car."

Eileen's red brows arched. "That isn't like you." She looked up at Clint. "Lisa is 'Miss Efficiency' at the office."

Without answering, Clint slowed and parked, leaving the motor idling to keep Eileen warm. His car lights were bright, piercing the darkness, lighting up the gray stockade fence that surrounded Lisa's small patio.

Fighting to keep her voice calm, Lisa told Eileen goodbye, and emerged into the cold. Clint accompanied her to the door. A small yellow light gleamed in the entranceway, and, carrying the pungent odor of wood burning, a thin stream of smoke curled from the chimney of a neighboring apartment. In silence, unable to express any of the turmoil seething inside her, Lisa walked beside Clint.

"Lisa, where's your door key?"

"I keep an extra one hidden underneath that flowerpot." She knelt quickly and retrieved it, then rose to face him. Clint's gray eyes rested on her. Like a wire stretched too tightly, her every nerve was taut with awareness of his physical presence.

"I watched the interview on television the other night," he remarked.

"Clint, I'd like to see you, to talk with you alone."

He misinterpreted her reason. "We need to, Lisa, before we get to that hearing. I don't relish facing you in a court fight." His voice sounded suddenly weary. "This whole thing is getting out of hand. I'm busy with appointments tomorrow." He paused to consider, then asked, "How about next Monday? I'll take you to lunch."

Disappointed at his suggestion, because Monday seemed years away, she started to ask him to see her sooner. But he spoke first.

"I won't take long, Lisa, just a little of your time."

"I just wanted to ask you if we could get together sooner, Clint."

"I don't know," he replied. "I don't think I can. Lisa, next time be more cautious. Getting snowbound was quite an antic. I don't know if you did it for more publicity or if you were just stubborn enough to buck a snowstorm, but—"

"Clint, I swear I didn't do that for publicity!" She fought the temptation to ignore Eileen, waiting in the car only yards away, and grasp his strong hands to cry, *"I love you! I'm here, if you want me back. I've been so foolish!"*

She spoke his name a second time. "Clint—"

"I know, I know—it's none of my business," he interrupted her, and pulled away, waving his hand. "Well, Lisa, before long I'll be out of your life forever." He paused and looked down at her. "I hope that makes you happy."

"Oh, Clint . . ." She reached out and caught his hand. His expression changed, and he looked at her intently.

At that moment Tom Perkins rounded the corner. "Lisa!" he cried, rushing over to hug her. "My God, we've been so worried!"

chapter 13

QUICKLY LISA WRENCHED AWAY, and met Clint's frosty stare. Tom turned and grasped his hand, shaking it vigorously. "Thanks, Callaway, I really appreciate what you did. That was big of you to rise above your differences and look for your wife." While he talked, he unfastened a camera in a case hanging around his neck. "How about a picture?"

Clint's features hardened. Without pausing for an answer, Tom raised the camera and stepped back.

"No pictures," Clint growled.

A quick flash blinded Lisa. "Tom, please...I don't want my picture in the paper this way..."

"I don't want to see that picture in the paper," Clint commanded. His voice was quiet, but it carried a cold authority that could not be mistaken. Tom Perkins's face flushed.

"Sure, Callaway, if you feel that strongly about it..."

Clint didn't wait to listen. He strode back to the car. Lisa's heart felt squeezed with longing. She wanted to call to him, to tell him to come back, but it was impossible. Clint slid in beside Eileen, and they drove away.

Close to tears, Lisa struggled to keep her voice normal. "I'm so exhausted, Tom. Please, I have to get some rest."

He quickly snapped a picture. "Lisa, this will be great. I've been so worried about you. I called Eileen, and she called Callaway, then I talked to him. When reports began to come in over the television and radio of motorists stranded by the sudden storm, I had to know whether or not you were safe."

She barely heard his words. Her thoughts were on the black Ferrari, on Clint and Eileen. Where had they gone—to Clint's apartment, or to Eileen's? She was too preoccupied even to protest the picture Tom took. "Tom, I'm exhausted," she murmured. "I'll call you tomorrow."

He patted her shoulder. "You rest. I'll call you later and hear what happened. Where's your car?"

"South of Mooreland. I slid off the highway into a snowbank." She unlocked the door. "Good night, Tom." She glanced down at the camera. "I don't look very nice. I'd rather you didn't print those pictures, please."

He winked. "I won't put anything in the paper that isn't flattering." He put his hand on her waist. His voice dropped. "Lisa, you don't have on make-up and your hair is tousled, yet you still look extremely desirable. No one would guess by looking that you've just been through an ordeal."

He leaned forward, but Lisa stepped away. "I'll see you, Tom."

He smiled and said good night. Lisa closed the door and slipped the lock into place. She felt numb with exhaustion, with disappointment, with longing for Clint. She thought how strong, masculine, and appealing he had looked in the parka and jeans. She wanted his arms around her. She longed to hear his voice, the husky note it had in moments of love. She glanced at the phone and for an instant debated calling, then realized she might get Eileen instead of Clint. She headed for the bathroom, wishing she could forget all her problems.

The night seemed long before she finally fell asleep. When she awakened, she decided to try to keep too busy to think about Clint.

But everything reminded her of him. When she unfolded the morning paper, page twelve had a small picture of her stepping to the door of her apartment. Contrary to what Tom had told her, she felt it was not particularly flattering. It showed little of her face, for which she was thankful, but she wished he hadn't even put it in the paper. The article was captioned with words concerning the snowstorm, but beneath it, in a small paragraph, Tom mentioned the fight to save the lake.

Lisa lowered the paper and ran her hand across her forehead. Something else to anger Clint.

During the day the temperature climbed above freezing. In the afternoon Lisa accepted Tom's insistent offer to drive her to pick up her car.

How different everything looked only a day later. The highway was bare. Across yellow fields, white patches glistened against fence posts and in ditches. A strong wind blew across the flat, open land and bent low the dried winter grass.

All during the drive Lisa found it increasingly difficult to keep her attention on Tom's words. Finally, stubbing out a cigarette in the ashtray, he glanced at her. "What are you thinking? You're not with me."

She sighed and looked down. "I'm sorry, Tom. So much has happened lately..."

He squeezed her shoulder. "It's Callaway, isn't it?" There was a note of surprise in his voice.

She looked up at him and nodded. "I'm not going to ask for a divorce."

Tom frowned. "That isn't what you told me before. Eileen said it was definite, that both you and Callaway agreed to a divorce."

It was difficult to utter the words. She looked out the window. "I won't get one. Clint will."

After a moment of silence, Tom asked, "You're still in love with him, aren't you?"

"Yes."

"Does he know?"

Lisa shrugged. "I don't think he cares."

"Does this mean the battle is over? That you're dropping your fight against the highway at the lake?"

She shook her head. "No. I still think they shouldn't build there."

For a few minutes the only sound was the hum of the motor, then Tom said carefully, "You know, Eileen thinks it's all over between you and your husband."

Lisa smoothed her coat over her knees. "It probably is, as far as Clint is concerned." She straightened and leaned forward. "There's my car—see it to the left?"

"Sure enough," he replied, and slowed, then made a sweeping turn to pull up facing the same direction as Lisa's car. He cut the motor, then shifted to look at her.

"Lisa, would you like some advice?"

With her hand on the latch, poised to step out, Lisa stopped and looked at him. "What's that?"

"Eileen is a user. She goes after what she wants when she decides she wants it. She's after your husband right now."

"I know," Lisa answered.

"If you don't want her to end up as the second Mrs. Clint Callaway, you'd better do something."

Lisa forced a thin smile. "Let's see about my car."

In half an hour they had the car back on the highway, and Lisa was ready to drive home.

Lisa declined Tom's offer to go to dinner. The evening and next day passed slowly, until Monday came, and the time for her lunch appointment with Clint.

Shortly after her arrival at the office, he called to confirm the date. She felt a rush of warmth as she listened to his mellow voice over the phone.

"Clint, I've found another folder of information about the wildlife at the lake as well as studies about a similar situation two years after a highway was built."

"Fine. Bring that along to lunch. I'll see you at noon, Lisa."

She hung up and went back to work until the hands

on the clock showed five minutes before it was time to meet Clint. Lisa grabbed the folder and hurried to the ladies' room.

Facing the mirrored wall, she checked her appearance one more time. The pale-blue wool dress heightened the blue of her eyes. Its straight lines and narrow skirt were plain and tailored, like most of her clothes. Clint used to prefer that she wear blue. She smoothed two thin gold chains that hung around her neck and added a delicate sparkle to the dress.

Every golden hair was in place, combed into a chignon behind her head. She thought fleetingly of Eileen's voluptuous looks. Lisa had been surprised that morning when Eileen appeared at work. Eileen carefully avoided any encounters with Lisa, and Lisa could only speculate on whether or not Eileen had turned in her resignation.

Lisa shrugged and picked up the folder as well as her coat, then hurried out to meet Clint.

Her palms were damp with nervousness. She felt like a schoolgirl waiting for her first date, and the impact she experienced when she caught sight of Clint did nothing to calm her nerves.

When she turned the corner of the hall, she discovered him in the reception room, talking with Eileen. At the thought that she would have to share him all through lunch, Lisa's heart sank.

As Lisa approached them, Eileen glanced over her shoulder. For a fleeting moment her back was to Clint. Her eyes narrowed coldly and she said, "I hear you and Clint have a lunch date."

Before Lisa could answer, Clint reached out and took Eileen's arm, saying easily, "The car is parked at the curb, Lisa. I'll be right out."

There was nothing to do but leave the office and wait for him. Soon Clint and Eileen approached the double glass doors. Lisa's heart wrenched at the sight of Clint's arm draped carelessly across Eileen's shoulder, of Eileen walking close by his side. Her lavender dress clung to her lush figure, the material shifting and twisting with each step.

They emerged from the office, and Clint turned Eileen to face him, his arm still draped lightly over her shoulder. Wind blew his black hair away from his face. His gray suit fit perfectly across his broad shoulders, tapering to a slim waist and lean hips. Even in a business suit, a tough vitality seemed to radiate from him.

Lisa felt as if a knife were turning inside as she watched them talking together. With a provocative movement, Eileen caught Clint's neck and pulled him close for a kiss, then stepped back to say something else to him.

He smiled and touched her chin lightly with his fist, then turned toward the car.

Lisa looked quickly down at her hands, fighting back tears. There was no question that he was attracted to Eileen. The whole luncheon date was useless. She might just as well save them both time and get out of the car, yet she couldn't bring herself to do so, to leave his company.

Struggling to get her emotions under control, she straightened the yellow folder in her lap, adjusting the loose pages inside it.

A rush of cold air entered with Clint. He reached into his pocket and withdrew a cigarette. "Care if I smoke, Lisa?"

"No," she murmured, not trusting her voice. Gone were all her intentions to confess her love even if she knew it was not returned.

After watching Eileen and Clint kiss, she couldn't utter the words. Too well, she could imagine his derisive laughter, his mocking sarcasm and amusement. She couldn't cope with that and had no intention of crying in his presence.

They rode in silence; smoke from Clint's cigarette filled the car until he opened the window a crack. Wind was blowing briskly in a chill, gray day. Lisa huddled in her coat, at a loss for words.

In a short time they reached the same Mexican restaurant Clint had taken her to before. After the waitress had left with their order, Clint took the folder from Lisa's hands.

He scanned the page. "The hearing is in two weeks." He looked up, and his gray eyes were piercing. "We've had to put a secretary on a line to handle calls asking us to refuse the job. Your campaign has been very effective."

Lisa noticed a strain of worry in his voice. "Is that what's bothering you?" she asked.

His gray eyes looked troubled. "Sometimes I think everything is wrong. Dad left the company in a bad situation. We have several contracts to fill, yet the necessary equipment isn't available." He ran his fingers through his thick hair. "We need new equipment, and the books are in terrible shape. I don't know. Every time I set foot in that office it's first one emergency, then another."

While they ate, he related the details of the company that were worrying him. All the time she listened, Lisa kept remembering his standing with Eileen, his arm around her shoulders, then Eileen reaching up on tiptoe to kiss him. Lisa found it difficult to get down even half the lunch.

Clint noticed and asked her about it.

Lisa shook her head. "I'm not very hungry, Clint."

His gray eyes were intent as he studied her. "Why not?"

She wanted to cry out that it was because Eileen had kissed him, but she couldn't say it. Instead she merely shrugged. "I don't know."

He gazed at her for a moment in silence. Lisa felt as if he could see through her, and looked down to avoid his penetrating gaze.

He signaled for the check, and they rose to leave. When Clint held her coat, she felt his fingers brush the back of her neck in a touch that made her skin tingle. She longed to reach up and touch his hand. Impulsively, she smoothed the collar of her coat, and their hands met for an instant. Clint seemed to pay no heed, and moved away.

Once in the car, he turned on the heater and drove into heavy traffic toward Lake Dodson. Lisa rode with her hands locked tightly in her lap, while she wished she could say all the things bottled up inside her.

"I think it's going to snow soon," Clint remarked, staring at the overcast sky. "I've talked long enough about trouble at the office. Go ahead and read the rest of the information to me."

While they sped along the freeway, Lisa obliged. She read about nesting habits and sightings of the least bittern, from April to October, the common loon in summer, the great blue heron and killdeer.

He glanced at her. "You know, Lisa, that's a man-made lake. Fifteen years ago those birds roosted on other mud flats."

She lowered the paper. "Nevertheless, Clint, they're here now, and many people don't want to see them frightened away."

They turned at the lake, and Lisa closed the folder to look at the water as Clint drove down a dry stretch of red earth, deeply rutted from snow, that would be part of the proposed roadway.

Near the water's edge, Clint stopped, and for a moment they gazed in silence at the gray, rolling water. High waves with large whitecaps swept into the shore to crash against slabs of rocks. Cottonwoods with dark, bare limbs fringed the edge of the lake.

Clint stepped out and walked around the car to open Lisa's door. "Want to get out for a moment?"

They were on a promontory that jutted out sufficiently to enable them to get a clear view of the west boundary of the lake. Clint's steely eyes narrowed as he studied the terrain.

Feeling a stab of longing that made her tremble, Lisa gazed at him. His rugged features were chiseled against the sky. The wind tangled his black curls.

She longed to cry out her love for him, yet there was no way to forget his parting kiss to Eileen. Would he laugh at her, fling the words back in her face?

The declaration died in her throat; she couldn't bear to face those mocking eyes.

Instead, she merely talked about the lake and birds. Clint's reply was caught by the wind. Lisa moved closer to hear.

"At the next board meeting we'll prepare for the hearing." He faced her squarely and spoke with a cynical note in his voice; his eyes were opaque and cold. "Lisa, I've been told you've definitely stated you're doing this to get revenge for what I've done."

"It's not true!" she cried. "I've never said that or done anything for that reason. Who told you that?"

His voice hardened. "I have no intention of revealing that to you."

"Don't you think that's a little unfair!" she snapped.

"Not in the least," he replied curtly. "It was told to me in confidence, and I won't violate that trust."

Filled with aggravation at his unreasonable attitude, she turned her coat collar up against the chilly wind coming off the water. "Suppose the person is lying? I think you're being unfair. I've never said that to anyone."

"Lisa, it would hurt you to know who told me. It's someone you like," he stated quietly.

She caught her breath and stared at him in surprise. The first person she could think of was Tom. "I don't believe you, Clint! You're making that up."

He raised a hand. "I swear to you, Lisa. Someone told me you've admitted it's only revenge."

The longing she had felt only a short time earlier was gone, replaced by mounting anger that he would attribute such low motives to her, as well as irritation that he was accepting a falsehood and hiding the speaker's identity.

"I swear to you, Clint Callaway, I never did any of this for such a reason! It's ridiculous for you to believe anyway. I couldn't stop the project, no matter what I did, and I haven't really hurt the company image, I'm sure."

He shook his head. "Oh, I don't know about that, Lisa. Corporations are much more susceptible to public opinion than you might think. Especially a company as small as ours."

"Now, Clint, Callaway isn't a little company."

"We're not small compared to many, but compared to the big national companies, we're small. We have offices here, in New Mexico, and in Peru. I don't know if we'll have all those much longer; we're facing hard times because of my father's mismanagement, but as far as this is concerned—if you're after revenge, I want to know."

Anger and hurt filled her. "I think you made that up, Clint. I don't believe anyone said any such thing. You can't believe I'm doing this out of sincere motives because you don't want to!"

Biting off each word with clipped emphasis, he stated forcefully, "I didn't make any of it up."

Lisa clenched her fists. Seething with anger, she snapped, "No one's heard me say I want revenge, because it isn't so. It's your own blind and stubborn way of holding on to what you want to believe!"

His eyes flashed with a dangerous glint, and he reached out to grasp her shoulders roughly. "Lisa, someone you trust has sworn to me that you've admitted this."

"Get your hands off me, Clint!" She wrenched free of his hold and stood facing him, gasping with fury.

His piercing eyes hardened to slate. "At least all that damn icy reserve is going."

"I need to get back to the office," she declared. "There's no point in standing out here arguing over this. I know what I've said and what I haven't said. I don't lie, Clint, even though you seem to think so!"

His jaw tightened in anger, but she didn't wait to hear his retort. She stomped through the high weeds to the car.

Clint jumped in beside her, his gray eyes frosty with anger. "Lisa, when will you grow up and stop running away from even discussing things? I don't know how you get through a day at the office."

"I'll tell you how," she stated in a low voice that quivered with rage. "I'm not accused of lying. I'm not manhandled!"

"Manhandled!" He turned to glare at her. "I'll show you what manhandling is!" His arm was around her waist in an instant, and he yanked her hard against him. His mouth silenced her protest, his kiss forceful, passionate. He bent her backwards, then shifted quickly so that he lay on top of her on the car seat.

Lisa fought angrily against him. Panic swept over her; she feared she would lose all control and make a fool of herself with him. She reminded herself that little more than an hour earlier she had watched him kiss Eileen.

His kiss was fiery and demanding. His hands shoved open her coat. She was filled with anguish, longing, and pain at the thought that he was acting out of anger, not love. She twisted violently. "Clint, stop!" she snapped. "I have to go back to work...."

He raised his head slightly and studied her. With a swift movement, she wriggled out of his grasp and sat up to scoot against the door. She glanced angrily at him while she straightened her clothes. "I can't walk into the office looking like this!" He sat up too and pulled out a pack of cigarettes. His unrumpled calm aggravated her even more.

She reached up to turn the rearview mirror so that she could gaze into it. "You don't have to worry about your hair..." She glanced at him as he raised a cigarette lighter, and she was startled to notice a tremor in his hands. He looked at her, and she turned away quickly. So their kiss had stirred him more than he would admit....

She gazed at her mouth, full and red from his kisses. Her chignon was hopelessly tangled. She pulled out the pins and dropped them into her lap, then removed a brush from her purse to straighten her hair.

Clint stubbed out the cigarette and turned on the ignition. He swung the car in a vicious circle, causing them to bounce wildly over the rough, uneven ground, then raced toward the main road.

Lisa snatched the pins that jiggled in her lap and bit back an angry request for him to slow down. She knew it would be useless.

The Ferrari lurched and skidded violently before careening onto the paving with a loud squeal of tires. Lisa closed her eyes, then opened them as the car straightened. She regarded Clint's savage profile.

"Now, who are you to talk about growing up? That was as juvenile as anything I've witnessed in a long time." She brushed her hair furiously and gathered it up behind her head once again. "I look as if I've been tumbled in the seat of a car!"

They rode in silence a moment; then he glanced at her. "It seems to me, Lisa, that you wouldn't be so angry if I hadn't confronted you with the truth."

"Why shouldn't I be angry?" she retorted. "You believed it, obviously. That's the insult. I can't believe anyone actually told you such a thing." As soon as she uttered the words, she guessed who was behind them—

Eileen. She glanced at Clint, speculating.

After a moment she said, "I know one person who might have told you that—Eileen. Is that right, Clint?"

His gaze remained on the road. "I'm not dragging Eileen or anyone else into this, Lisa. That isn't what's important."

Resenting his protection of Eileen, she stared back at him, hurt and angry. "You're very loyal to her, Clint."

A muscle in his jaw twitched, and he hunched his powerful shoulders slightly as they raced along the freeway. Suddenly a siren sounded and a red light blinked steadily behind them. Clint swore softly, slowed the car, and pulled over to the curb.

A patrol car parked behind him, and a policeman stepped out. Clint's knuckles were white on the steering wheel.

"It serves you right, Clint Callaway!" Lisa murmured.

The patrolman gazed in the window.

"Going a little fast, mister? Oh, Mr. Callaway!"

The officer's scowl disappeared, and he pushed his cap to the back of his head.

"Mike Washington!" Clint greeted him, and opened the door to step out. "I was speeding," he admitted. He shook hands with the policeman.

After he closed the door, his words became muffled, but Lisa could hear him say, "I've had a fight with my wife, Mike, and I forgot to watch my speed." Lisa listened to Clint's easy laugh. "I suppose my speed rose with my temper."

"Yep, I guess that can happen. I'll tell you what, Mr. Callaway. You're new in the States, being back such a short time and all. I'll issue you a warning ticket this time."

Clint shook his head. "I was over the limit; I know that."

"I'll issue the warning, then you take it easy—on the speed, that is."

"Okay, thanks." Clint continued to talk to the man about bowling, then climbed back into the car. He glanced at Lisa. "No fine," he stated. "Much to your disappointment, I'm sure."

"You deserved a ticket."

He eased the car into traffic. Finally he said, "Will you please leave the folder for me to study?"

"Yes, but I see little use in it. You're not going to change your mind. It sounds like your company needs all the business it can get—whether scrupulous or not."

His strong hands tightened on the steering wheel. "Oh, come off it, Lisa! I'd hardly call this unscrupulous. Most people had no idea that the highway would damage wildlife."

She rode in silence a moment, then said, "I don't see how you can believe such a thing about me, Clint. That's insult enough to make anyone angry."

He slowed, and stopped in front of her office, then shifted to face her. His smoky eyes rested on her, and he spoke quietly. "It was Eileen."

The statement cut her like a knife. "You'd take her word over mine—" she cried.

"Lisa," he interrupted, "that's why I told you—"

"Clint, you're impossible!" she cried, and slid out of the car.

"Lisa!" he called after her.

She glanced down. "Here," she snapped, "take the folder! I'm sure it will go straight to the trash!" She flung it toward the car seat, but it careened off the edge of the open door and hit Clint in the face. Papers flew over the front seat.

Lisa turned and raced into the building, hurrying past the startled receptionist to her own office, where she closed the door immediately.

Hot tears stung her eyes and rolled down her cheeks. She hadn't done anything right during the entire time with him. She hadn't told him about not wanting a divorce, much less that she loved him. Why did she always get all tied up in knots when she was with him? It was hopeless.

Lisa moved woodenly to her desk and sat down, wiping her eyes with a handkerchief. How badly she had handled the meeting! If only she'd remained calm—but remaining calm around Clint was an impossible task.

chapter 14

THE REST OF the week passed swiftly until Friday night, when Lisa's spirits sank even lower. The departmental banquet was being held that night, and she knew Eileen would appear with Clint.

With care, Lisa put on a clinging white dress with bare shoulders, adding two thin strands of gold around her neck. Her hair gleamed and smelled fresh from apricot shampoo. She brushed it vigorously into a smooth pageboy. As she stared at her reflection in the mirror, her blue eyes seemed larger than ever, with the long golden hair hanging down to curl softly across her shoulders.

Finally she was ready. She paced back and forth until Tom appeared, punctually at seven o'clock. With the camera on the car seat between them, they drove to a tall building and entered, past a fountain in the lobby. Music played softly from a speaker as they rode the elevator to a large room on the top floor decorated in deep red and dark brown.

Office policy required that employees attend, particularly those receiving awards, but Lisa, distressed at the prospect of watching Clint with Eileen, longed to be home. She wished she'd never consented to allow Tom to cover the event for the newspaper; it would be one more thing to aggravate Clint.

She thought of the coming hearing with City Council members, the commissioners from the Transportation

Commission, local members of the Audubon Society, residents who lived around the lake area, the press, Callaway company representatives—and especially Clint.

How could she fight Clint in a public hearing? She wasn't certain she could do it, yet it was impossible to think of dropping the proposal. Nearly a dozen calls a day were coming into the office now in support of the lake. Tom had reported that the paper was receiving just as many. Her thoughts were interrupted by Tom's leaning close.

"Lisa, since you're getting an award, where are you supposed to sit?"

She motioned to a table at one end of the room where small place cards designated their seats. She had been placed directly in front of the table for department heads and speakers. At the opposite end of the room was a small stage and dance floor.

Lisa and Tom sat down at a table with her secretary and Nancy's husband, Bill. Lisa scanned the crowd but failed to see any sign of Clint or Eileen.

A crowd had filled the room by the time Eileen and Clint arrived. There was no mistaking their entrance; Clint's dark head and shoulders were easily detected above a throng of people clustered at the door. His dark-blue suit and white shirt made his skin appear a deep bronze and added to an impression of ruthless sophistication.

As noticeable as Clint was Eileen in a skintight, flesh-colored dress with a plunging neckline that left little to the imagination.

Lisa looked away quickly, but not before she'd met Clint's glance. She was certain she saw anger burning in his eyes as he stared back at her.

Although she had known all along that he would appear with Eileen, actually seeing them together shocked her into silence.

Tom's voice reached her, and she turned to him.

"You'd make a good poker player, Lisa. No one would ever know you felt anything."

"Tom..." It was difficult to say the words. "...I'd rather not talk about it."

"Okay," he answered blithely, and patted her hand, then continued, "but if you want that guy, you'd better go after him, because Eileen sure as hell is."

"Tom..."

He waved his hand. "I'll be quiet on the subject. We ought to get some good shots tonight. Will you make a speech when you accept your award?"

She laughed. "No. All I want to do is thank everyone and sit down."

"Do me a favor and pause up there. Let me get several pictures. Okay?"

When she hesitated, he leaned closer and put his hand on her arm. "Lisa, I'll level with you. I'm trying to land a job with one of the television stations. This story of yours is keeping my name on the front page, and it's helping my career." He patted her arm. "I'm interested in your cause, don't misunderstand, but it's been to my benefit. It's just the kind of human-interest story that catches everybody's attention. I'll know this time next week whether I'm getting the job or not, so bear with me a little longer. Okay?"

She sighed and, without thinking, looked up to meet Clint's frosty gaze across the crowd. Quickly, she looked at Tom again. "Very well," she answered quietly.

"Hey, don't sound so formal. Look, Lisa, I meant it when I said that I've been interested in your fight. I really have," he insisted.

She smiled. "I believe you, Tom."

Suddenly he was intent as he placed his arm around her shoulders and faced her. His knees pressed against hers; his face was only inches away.

"Look," he said earnestly, "you're the one who said

no. If there's a chance, I'll be happy to step in, but when I tried, I didn't get to first base with you. Is there a chance?"

Before she could answer, he laughed. "I'm always ready for a good time. I don't care for anything serious or permanent—look what it brought you. But, honey, if there's a chance you can forget that guy, just let me know."

Lisa laughed. "I'll remember that, Tom."

"Will you pause up there long enough for me to get my shots?"

She nodded, and he patted her shoulder. "That's my gal!" He leaned forward and kissed her cheek, then settled back to allow a waiter to place a bowl of steaming soup before him.

As if drawn by a magnet, Lisa turned and looked across the tables, directly into Clint's hooded eyes. It was a shock to gaze into their angry, gray depths.

Eileen turned to say something to him, and Clint laughed, shifting slightly to face her. An ache curled and wound through Lisa as she watched Eileen reach up and brush back a lock of Clint's dark hair that tumbled on his forehead.

All appetite gone, she looked down at a bowl of brown onion soup, unable to swallow anything. She nibbled at the food throughout dinner but left most of the thick steak untouched.

The constant sight of Clint leaning close to Eileen, his large, strong hand against her back, his gray eyes dancing with amusement as he laughed at something she said, was more than Lisa could stand to watch.

When she had finished eating, and before the speeches began, she excused herself to go to the powder room.

In the silence of the pink-and-green mirrored room, she ran a comb through her hair. Behind her the door opened, and Lisa glanced in the mirror to see Eileen behind her. For the past week Eileen had carefully avoided Lisa. This was their first confrontation since the trip home from Lisa's stranded car.

Lisa murmured hello, then looked down to put her comb away.

Eileen's voice was cool as she remarked casually, "Hello, Lisa." She paused, then added, "I've turned in my resignation at the office."

Lisa headed for the door, but she turned to look at Eileen. "I wondered if you had." The knowledge that Eileen would now work for Clint added another grim touch to the evening.

Eileen's green eyes glittered, and she tossed her head. "I intend to marry Clint when he gets divorced."

The declaration was like a knife turning inside Lisa. She couldn't reply. Blinded by tears, she turned quickly and left the room. She tried to regain her composure as she hurried down the hall toward the banquet room.

She rounded the corner and collided into someone. Arms steadied her, and she looked up at Clint.

"Lisa!" He regarded her intently. "I want to talk to you."

It took an effort to speak, but she said, "Eileen's already told me."

"I came because I want to see you get that award."

Her throat hurt; everything seemed to ache, and she prayed that the tears didn't show. Clint was studying her so intently that she was afraid he'd guess she was in turmoil.

Her words sounded stiff and cold. "Tom's waiting, Clint."

"All right." He leaned forward to look at her closely. "You don't look happy, Lisa," he said quietly.

Wanting to cry out the reason—that she loved him and didn't want a divorce—Lisa bit her lip. She forced a smile to her lips. "I'm fine, Clint." She moved away before he could say more. What else was there to say? She couldn't blurt out the truth—it would be useless to do so, and embarrassing to him.

A public dinner was no place for a personal discussion. Besides, Eileen would reappear at any moment and claim Clint.

Lisa slid into her seat. She found it difficult during the next hour to keep her attention on the speakers. She rose and went forward to receive her award for articles she'd written promoting conservation in Oklahoma. She expressed her gratitude for the award.

In spite of her effort to avoid looking at Clint, she gazed over the crowd and looked into his eyes. He was leaning back in his chair with his long legs stretched out before him. His hooded eyes were inscrutable as he returned her gaze.

Lisa turned away and resumed her seat. Tom leaned close to kiss her cheek. "Congratulations, Lisa! I got my pictures." He looked at the plaque. "When the speeches are over, let's get one more closeup of you and the award."

She agreed, and soon the awards were finished, the music started, and she stepped into the hall so that Tom could take her picture. As soon as he was finished, she asked if they could leave.

"I don't feel like dancing, Tom. I'm sorry."

He shrugged. "I don't mind. Come on, I'll get our coats." He tilted his head to one side as he took her arm. "It's Eileen, isn't it?"

She nodded. While she was waiting for him to return from the coatroom, Lisa glanced in the long mirror that reflected through the open archway and caught the dancers. In the mirror she saw Eileen in Clint's arms, laughing into his face, moving sensuously against him in the tight dress.

Eileen molded her body to Clint's, against the hard

muscular thighs, along his lean hips and broad, powerful chest—against the body that Lisa knew so well, that had lain naked against her own, his flesh against hers.

Feeling as if a thousand daggers were stabbing into her heart, Lisa moved to Tom's side, away from the mirror and away from the open door. Within minutes they were heading home.

At her apartment, Tom let the motor idle and turned to face her. He reached out to take her hand and pull her toward him.

Lisa resisted. "Tom, I'd better go in. . . ."

He laughed and settled back against the door. "Relax, Lisa. You can't blame me for trying." He patted the camera in the back seat. "I'll have a story out about you in the morning paper. How about going with me for breakfast, and we'll get an early edition?"

"How can you get tonight's pictures in so quickly?" she asked with surprise.

"I can't. It's another story, written before the banquet. How about breakfast?"

She shook her head. "Thank you, but no. Tom, I don't think we should keep seeing each other. You said tonight that you needed my story. I hope it helped you get the job you want, but I've had enough publicity."

He smiled and ran his hand across her cheek. "And there isn't any other reason for us to see each other?"

"Tom—" she began, but he interrupted.

"Forget it, Lisa. I'm looking for a good time, and you're a very earnest girl." He leaned forward and kissed her lightly, then stepped outside and came around the car.

At the door of her apartment, he stopped. "Lisa, would you like some advice?"

"Yes," she answered with a smile.

"If you really love Callaway, go after him. I know Eileen as well as I know myself. We dated for a long time, then mutually agreed to part. She's a tough woman, and she'll stop at nothing to get what she wants. Where men are concerned, she has no scruples. She has few women friends—you were one of the few, because you posed no threat to her. She wants him—she's told me that. She said that all the time he was in South America, you were trying to get over him. . . ."

"That was true, Tom. I thought it was over between us."

"I don't think it would have made any difference to her," he continued.

Lisa patted his arm. "Thanks for the advice, Tom." She did not care to discuss her problems with Tom. She thanked him and went inside. The rest of the weekend she waited to receive a call from Clint confirming the commencement of divorce proceedings.

When she returned to work on Monday, she was still expecting a call. Instead, she received a surprise from her secretary, Nancy.

"Congratulations, Lisa!" she cried. "You won your battle."

Lisa gazed at her, perplexed. "What are you talking about?"

At that moment Mr. Spradling, her supervisor, appeared. "Congratulations, Lisa. You fought a stiff battle." He smiled and waved, then disappeared into his office once more.

"Will somebody tell me what's going on?" Lisa demanded.

In amazement, Nancy asked, "You really don't know?"

Lisa tried to control her impatience. "Nancy, what is it?"

Without a word Nancy thrust the paper into her hands. "Here, Lisa, read this."

She glanced down at *The Press*, a weekly paper devoted to more sensational reporting than the daily paper. Bright print jumped out at her: ENGINEER YIELDS PROJECT TO SAVE MARRIAGE.

With each word a leaden weight grew inside Lisa, as she read that Clint had withdrawn from the highway project in order to save their marriage. Stunned, she read the sentence that indicated she was the source of this information.

With implication, innuendo and hints—and no direct quotations—the article conveyed a very false message.

"I thought you dated that reporter from the daily paper," Nancy stated.

Lisa glanced at the secretary. "This isn't true at all," she murmured.

Nancy's eyes grew round. "You mean you didn't say that—and your husband didn't either?"

"No," Lisa stated, certain that the article would be as big a surprise to Clint as to herself. "I didn't know anything about this. It's completely untrue!"

"That's terrible!" Nancy exclaimed.

Lisa merely nodded and carried the paper into her office. After closing the door, she spread the paper on her desk and read the article once again. With each line her horror increased. Without being near him, she could feel Clint's wrath. And she wouldn't blame him. The article was damning—its veiled words hinting that Lisa had extracted a promise from Clint to withdraw from the highway project in exchange for a reconciliation.

Eyes open wide, Lisa looked up and stared into space. Was Eileen behind this?

She reached for the phone. The most important thing was to talk to Clint, to let him know she hadn't told the paper such things.

At his office the secretary informed her that Mr. Callaway was out of the office and could not be reached.

Instantly Lisa guessed that Clint could be on his way

to her office. She wouldn't blame him for rushing over to confront her with the story.

But she didn't want such a confrontation to take place in front of her boss. Clint was slow to anger, but if he reached the boiling point, everyone would know it. Lisa snatched up her purse and coat and raced for the door.

She hurried down the hall to Nancy's desk and explained breathlessly, "Nancy, I have to leave right now, but I'll call when I get home."

The slender brunette glanced up, then frowned. "Lisa, you look like you're going to faint. Can I have someone drive you home?"

She shook her head. Out of the corner of her eye she caught sight of a dark car stopping at the curb. Her heart lurched wildly, but the driver wasn't Clint.

"No, thanks, Nancy. I'll call as soon as I get home." Lisa rushed outside, flinging her coat around her shoulders as she ran to the car. She slid behind the wheel, grasping it with trembling fingers as she backed out of her parking place.

chapter 15

NOT UNTIL SHE was a block from the office did Lisa's pulse begin to return to normal. She realized she had acted impulsively, yet she could easily imagine Clint's appearing at the office for a volatile confrontation.

If only she could reach him by telephone and make him listen to reason. She turned into the short drive at the back of her apartment, then rushed across the patio, once again feeling her heartbeat increase. She half expected to see Clint step forth.

She rushed through the empty apartment, then sat down on the bed to phone his office again. This time she left word for him to call her, hung up, and phoned her own office.

With crisp efficiency Nancy answered. As soon as she learned it was Lisa, she said, "Your husband was just here to see you. He talked with Eileen for a minute, before he left. She's packing things in her office."

"I need to talk to him, Nancy," Lisa said. "Do you know where he is now?"

"No, he didn't say. I told him you'd gone home."

"If he calls or comes back, please tell him to call me, that it's urgent."

"Okay," Nancy promised. "Do you feel all right?"

"Not particularly," Lisa answered truthfully. She promised to phone again later in the day, then hung up. There was nothing she could do until she reached Clint, but every moment of waiting was agony.

She slipped out of her coat and walked to the kitchen to put the kettle on for a cup of coffee. The article made Clint appear a fool, a man who indulged her every whim. He'd worried about his board of directors before; she wondered what this new turn of events would do to him.

She turned off the whistling teakettle and made a cup of instant coffee. While she drank it, she tried Clint's office once more, but he was still out. She hung up and sighed. If only there was something to do besides wait, knowing that somewhere out there, Clint was as upset as she...angrier, even, and growing more so by the minute.

Just then a knock sounded, a loud bang against her front door that caused her to jump with fright. She rushed to the door.

"Lisa!"

There was no mistaking Clint's voice. Her heart lurched violently. For the past forty minutes she had tried to reach him; now that he was only a few feet away, she feared the confrontation.

She straightened her shoulders and unlocked the door, then held it open.

He reached out and banged it wide, rushing in past her and flinging it closed behind him.

He was dressed in the same conservative, dark-blue suit she had seen him wear before, with a white shirt and dark tie. Over the suit he wore a heavy black topcoat. His face was savage, his gray eyes glittering satanically.

He faced her with his hands on his hips. "All right, Lisa," he snarled, "let's get this settled!"

"Clint, I didn't have anything to do with that article," she gasped.

"Like hell!" Glaring at her like the devil on a rampage, he snapped, "Don't give me that! You've really fixed me this time. My board of directors was none too happy with my coming up from South America and stepping in to replace the old boys Dad had surrounded himself with for the past twenty years. They're ruining the company but they don't want to let go, because it's theirs."

His clipped, biting tone stung her like a physical blow. "I've been fighting against them for my life," he continued, "trying by tact, brains, and luck to pull this company out of a slump. And now you do this to me!"

"Clint—" she began, but he interrupted.

"Dad wanted to run things his way. Equipment and methods were antiquated; we're in debt. Along comes this contract—a ripe plum that looks as good as gold—and my wife is about to destroy it. Needless to say, the board is less than happy with me for that reason alone. Add to that the changes I want to make, and it really gets sticky. Now this! If I sue the paper, it'll be a long hassle before it's cleared up."

"Clint, can't you tell them it's not true?"

"Certainly, Lisa, but it looks bad for the company. Other firms will be calling the Transportation Commission—I think it will weaken our stand at the hearing."

"Surely not!"

His eyes narrowed. "Maybe that's what you had in mind all along. Every time I turn around you're saying or doing something damaging, but this really takes the cake!" His anger vibrated in every searing word. "If you had sat and thought long and hard about some way to get even with me, I don't think you could have succeeded any better."

Her heart pounded wildly in the face of his anger, but she regarded him steadily and forced her voice to sound strong. "Clint, will you please listen to me? I didn't plant the story."

His eyes flashed fire. "Then who did, Lisa?"

"I don't know," she answered miserably, knowing how inadequate and unconvincing the words sounded. "I don't have any more idea than you. All I know is that I didn't."

"Don't try to pin this on Eileen," he warned her derisively. "She wouldn't speak to me this morning except to congratulate me on our reconciliation."

"I think she'll listen to your arguments," Lisa retorted. They stared at each other for a moment in silence, the tension between them becoming intolerable.

The piercing, slate-colored eyes held her pinned by their anger. "Lisa, it's bad enough that you would do such a thing"—his voice deepened with fury—"but then to stand there and deny it..."

"Clint, for all I know, Tom, Eileen, anyone could have told them that story," she replied curtly. "I am telling you the truth!"

He looked away in disgust, then back to her. "Come off it, Lisa. You did it and you want to dump the blame somewhere else." He sighed heavily. "I'll get a divorce as fast as possible, Lisa." His voice was a rasp of fury. "I called a lawyer before I came, and I'm supposed to see him in an hour. I'll give you that divorce; then I hope we never lay eyes on each other again!"

She wanted to cry out her protest, but in the face of his anger, the words died in her throat.

Clint's eyes narrowed. "You've won, Lisa. You've won, hands down!"

In almost tangible waves, she felt his rage. Defiantly, she stared at him. "I wasn't trying to 'win,' Clint. I never told any of that story to the paper—and that's the truth."

In a swift movement he closed the distance between them. Lisa's heart thudded, pulsating in a rapid drumming in her ears.

He shook her slightly as he snarled, "Now, I'm warning you, Lisa, stay out of my hair. We have the divorce and the hearing to fight out, but don't involve me in anything you do!"

All fear and remorse left her. His arrogance increased her anger. "Clint Callaway, don't threaten me! I've explained I had nothing to do with the newspaper story!" She raised her chin. "I'll get out of your life, just as you want, but take your hands off me and stop shaking me!"

"You're fortunate all I'm doing is shaking you," he answered. "If you were a man—"

"If I were," she interrupted in a tight voice, "I'd be glad to try to break that crooked nose of yours again, Clint Callaway! I've explained everything to you. I don't see any need to apologize for something I didn't do. Now, take your hands off me!"

He looked at her in silence but didn't move.

Her anger pouring out in clipped words, she said again, "I mean it. Take your hands off me! I'm tired of being shouted at for things I didn't do. I've had enough of your insinuations and accusations." She quivered with fury. "Get out of my apartment, Clint. I intended to call that paper to try to get a retraction out of them. I don't think I'll do one thing now. You can handle it in your own domineering way!"

"Lisa . . ."

Her voice throbbed with emotion. "Go back to Eileen. She'll forgive you, Clint. She thinks you're quite a catch and hangs on every word you say. She ought to be a sop to your ego!"

A muscle worked in his jaw; he stood so close that Lisa could detect the fragrance of his mint after-shave. The thick fringe of black lashes hooded eyes that were like chips of ice.

"Well, now, if we're talking about returning to someone—how about you and Perkins? He couldn't keep his hands off you at the banquet. I noticed both of you left early in the evening." His words were cold and cutting, his voice harsh. "It's not pleasant, Lisa, to come home from Peru and find my wife with another man. What did you do while I was gone?" he asked bitterly. "How many others have shared your favors?"

In a violent movement Lisa wrenched free and raised her hand to slap his face, in a blind rage.

His strong brown fingers closed around her wrist, and he regarded her intently. "That reserve is slipping, Lisa."

"How can you talk?" She tugged against his firm hold. "No one gets any more irate than you do, Clint!"

His gray eyes blazed with anger, but there was a look in his face that was impossible to understand. In defiance she gazed up at him. What was it about Clint that eluded her? It was impossible to guess his thoughts.

Suddenly he released her and turned on his heel, heading for the door.

Lisa picked up a vase and heaved it with all her might. It sailed over his shoulder and smashed against the door. White splinters bounced on the floor.

"Get out!" she cried. "I don't understand you, Clint, and I've had enough of your arrogant chauvinism!" She couldn't hold back the words. All her thoughts came blurting out. "We don't have anything in common. . . ."

His gray eyes flashed, and he closed the gap between them. "There's one damn thing we have in common," he growled. His hand cupped her head, and he slipped an arm around her waist to bend her beneath him as he kissed her.

His mouth claimed hers, his lips, his tongue tasting and demanding, giving a molten pleasure that transcended her anger. Unrelenting, as if he could destroy all their differences in fierce passion, he kissed her with a ravenous insistence that drove all the breath from her lungs. Her head reeled, and she felt weak in the knees.

Then the traitorous longing that he was attempting to provoke began to stir within her. The trembling giddiness began to change to blazing desire.

Lisa arched against him. A shudder rippled through his powerful body, and he released her.

His face was white, creased with tense lines around

his mouth. His gray eyes pierced her, and he whispered hoarsely, "Now tell me we don't have anything in common! I'm going to put an end to this, Lisa. . . ."

He whirled and was gone, slamming the door behind him with enough force to rattle the windowpanes.

Lisa shook violently as she stared at the blank door. Suddenly, the phone began to ring. As she moved to answer it, Lisa heard the motor of Clint's car roar loudly. She could picture his hands tightly gripping the wheel, the deep gray of his angry eyes.

Tom Perkins said hello and announced, "Lisa, I just saw the article in *The Press*. Congratulations on your reconciliation—I know that's what you wanted."

She fought against the hot tears that stung her eyelids, and tried to keep her voice normal. "I don't know anything about it, Tom."

His voice sounded strange. "It's not true?"

"No."

There was a pause; then he asked, "How did the paper get the story?"

"I don't know."

He sighed. "Would you like me to see what I can find out about it?"

"I don't think there's much use now," she replied. "Thanks for calling, though." She said goodbye and hung up; then, in spite of what she had told Clint, she dialed the office of *The Press* and told them that the article was not true. The reporter she talked to was not the one who had written the story. When Lisa asked for the person who had written it, she was told he was out of the office. After she had hung up, the tears she had held back for so long came streaming down her cheeks.

Lisa wiped her eyes and rose to return to the office. There was nothing to be gained by sitting in an empty apartment.

* * *

She spent the rest of the week in turmoil, thinking about Clint and making an effort to put him out of her mind. On Friday afternoon the electric power went out in a section of town that included Lisa's office, and they closed early.

When she reached home, she changed into a warm white knit shirt with long sleeves and a cowl neck, over dark-blue slacks. She stared into the mirror at the dark circles under her eyes, realizing it was from lack of sleep and loss of appetite; she had a hollow-eyed appearance.

She wondered vaguely how long it would take to get over Clint; she couldn't imagine ever forgetting him, yet life was becoming unbearable.

At the office she found herself making mistakes, careless miscalculations; she kept filing papers in the wrong places.

She only nibbled at the small dinner of meat loaf and salad she prepared for herself that night, then she cleaned the kitchen with a vengeance. At the sink she pushed aside the yellow organdy curtains to glance into the black night. A cold wind howled at the window. It was a relief to be in the haven of her apartment.

All week Lisa had been aware of Clint's promise to start divorce proceedings. In spite of the terrible fight she'd had with Clint, Lisa loved him, and the thought of Clint's being with Eileen filled her with pain and longing.

It had been four days since their violent quarrel. All her anger had disappeared, replaced by an ever-present sense of loss. It seemed an eternity since she'd been with him.

The shrill ring of the phone startled her; she lifted the receiver, to listen to a deep male voice.

Calmly, in a matter-of-fact tone, Clint said, "Lisa, I've come up with an alternative plan to present to my board of directors and the City Council. It may not do any good, because it may be too late to change anything."

Thinking of their last tumultuous encounter and wondering why he had called, she waited while he explained, "Would you mind if I picked you up and we drove by the site I'm proposing, to see what you think of it? It won't take long. Will you go?"

"I'll be glad to," she answered, trying not to sound breathless.

"Fine. I'll see you in a few minutes, if that's okay." His voice was a warm baritone filled with quiet confidence. Even his voice over the phone had an effect on her which was immediate and physical.

Lisa combed her hair, redoing the perfect chignon, and studied her flawless make-up, then rushed when she heard the bell. She caught up a gray jacket and gloves and opened the door.

Lisa didn't notice the blast of cold wind from the open door. Clint's gray eyes were solemn, unreadable.

Adding to his ruggedness, his thick black curls were tangled by the wind. A black turtleneck sweater showed at the open neck of his suede, fur-lined jacket; the heavy material added inches to his powerful shoulders and caused him to fill the doorway as he entered.

Lisa was vibrantly aware of him, of blue denims stretched tight across his muscled thighs. It was impossible not to react to his presence; she ached with longing for him.

"Ready?" he asked.

She nodded and stepped outside, as he reached around her and closed the apartment door, then fell into step at her side.

His car was cozy and warm, with frosted windows. As soon as she was seated, Lisa stretched out her legs and gazed into the darkness.

"This won't take long," Clint remarked. "I've been studying the lake, the residential area—the whole thing. I think I've found an alternative route that might be acceptable."

She turned in the seat to face him, looking at his harsh profile, the strong hands gripping the wheel. He withdrew a cigarette and lit it. The tip of the lighter glowed red. Clint exhaled a stream of smoke.

He reached into the back seat, glancing quickly over his shoulder. His hand brushed her shoulder as he twisted around.

The touch was feather-light, yet it burned through her layers of clothing. Lisa locked her fingers together and stared into the night.

He swore softly. When she glanced at him in surprise, he jerked his head toward the back seat. "Lisa, I can't reach the roll of papers in the corner."

She rose and leaned over the seat to pick up a roll of heavy paper fastened with a rubber band. Her side pressed against his shoulder as she stretched to it; she shifted and moved away. When she turned, she caught him looking at her with narrowed eyes. Instantly his attention returned to the highway.

"There's a flashlight in the glove compartment. Take it out and you can see where I've drawn a line around the lake."

Lisa did as he suggested. She turned on the light and unrolled the paper, which kept curling shut. Clint reached over to catch one side and hold it down. The cigarette was between his lips, a wisp of smoke rising from it. He squinted and glanced at the paper.

His hand lay on her leg, casually light, but Lisa was as aware of it as if it were a red-hot brand. She struggled to concentrate on the map, fighting down an awareness of his warm hand on her thigh.

He glanced quickly at the map. "See where I've drawn the line . . ."

The paper curled against his fingers; the circle of light from the unsteady flashlight in Lisa's hand jiggled with the movement of the car.

He swore softly. "Just wait until we get there, and I'll

point it out to you." He took the roll from her and dropped it into his own lap. Lisa turned off the flashlight and placed it on her lap.

Clint puffed on the cigarette; smoke wreathed his face for an instant, then disappeared. After a moment he stubbed it out and shut the ashtray with a snap which was loud in the taut silence between them.

The sleek car rolled smoothly along the paving until Clint signaled, slowed, and turned onto a rough, narrow road of asphalt that circled the lake.

Darkness closed in as they left behind the lights along the expressway. A thin sliver of new moon, like a silvery fragment of glass, glimmered dimly in the black sky. Lisa glanced out the side window at the lonely expanse of land and water.

The car slowed and stopped. Lisa looked at Clint in surprise. "Why are we stopping here?"

"I just want to show you these plans; then we'll drive around that way." A cold blast of wind hit the car and rocked it slightly.

Clint picked up the flashlight and handed her the roll of paper. His hands brushed her lightly as he instructed, "Unroll that side, while I hold this one." He shifted closer, raising the flashlight to illuminate the chart.

Lisa gazed at the map, far more aware of his length pressed against her, his thigh, warm through layers of clothing, touching hers, the hard calf of his leg against hers, and his face only inches away.

She struggled to keep her attention on his words and on the map.

His strong hand pointed at the lines. "See, here, Lisa, this in where the proposed road will lie—around the west side of the lake. Now, what I'd like to suggest is a highway around the east side."

"But that's out of the way!" she exclaimed, looking up at him.

He raised his head; his mouth was inches from hers.

She could think only of the feel of his lips, not of a lake or a road or a map. Breathing was difficult, and it was with a concerted effort that she moved her gaze from his mouth.

Looking into his eyes was no better. He watched her intently as he talked, his fathomless gaze boring into her eyes until she feared he could see what she felt, that her emotions must be exposed to his piercing gray stare.

She looked down at the map and tried to pay attention to his deep voice.

"It is out of the way, and would have to cross the river that feeds into the lake, which is why no one considered it in the original study." He looked at her. "But at that time no one had brought up the problem of the environment." His attention shifted; he traced a line along the west side of the lake. Lisa felt his finger run along her thigh, and tingles went up her spine.

"This will be more costly, there's no question of that, but it may be the only workable solution." His finger slid across the paper, lightly rubbing her leg beneath it.

The fiery touch increased her physical response to him, until she ached to move closer, to wrap her arms around his neck and cling to him.

Instead, she sat immobile, her eyes on the paper, and prayed that he wouldn't hear her heart hammering.

How typical of Clint to study the issue thoroughly. She thought of his meticulous attention to detail, the methodical way he approached problems, the deliberate way he made love to her. There was always an awareness of her needs, consideration of her pleasure. Clint gave of himself in an effort to heighten her response. She struggled to get her mind back to the discussion.

She listened as he said, "On this side of the lake they already have construction, industry, a road that is fairly busy." He regarded her steadily. "What I want to know from you is if you think there'd be as much disturbance to the wildlife if the highway ran along that side."

It was impossible to think rationally. She stared at the map, forcing herself to think about his words. Slowly she decided he was correct in his assumptions about the lake. She answered without looking up at him, pointing to the map simply to avoid meeting those cool gray eyes, so close to her own, to avoid looking once again at his mouth.

"You might be right, Clint."

He shifted away from her and rolled up the map. "I don't know, Lisa. It would cost more, but the funding might be managed if the project is feasible. It would serve both interests to such an extent that it might be worth the additional cost."

He dropped the paper into his lap, then leaned across her, casually resting his arm on her knee as he opened the glove compartment to put away the flashlight.

He straightened and suggested, "Let's drive around there." He eased the car onto the road again. Lisa glanced at him. Light from the dashboard was reflected on his high cheekbones and the slight crook in his nose.

She spoke hesitantly. "Clint, has this actually been harmful to your business?"

He looked at her quickly. "It damn well hasn't helped. We want the job."

"I'm sorry for that," she said.

"It may work out yet." He stared into the darkness. "It hasn't been easy to come home and take over, but I'm finally getting things under control. I've hired some new people and made some changes I thought were necessary."

Lisa stared at him, unable to imagine Clint in any situation over which he did not have full control. "I bet, Clint, it's not as bad as you say," she said softly.

He raised an eyebrow. "It's not," he admitted. "But I've had to make drastic changes in a hurry. I was surprised at the condition Dad left things in. I didn't want to go to Peru, and we parted on very bad terms."

"I didn't know that," she said.

"We didn't have much communication after that. Dad could be very stubborn and autocratic."

"Surely no more than his son," she said, without thinking, then wished she could retract the words. "I'm sorry, Clint. That wasn't kind."

He turned to study her, before turning back to the road. "Maybe I deserved it," he replied. "Dad and I didn't talk much, and I had no notion what the situation was with the business here."

Silence filled the car as he turned up a small incline to the dam, then drove slowly across it. Lisa gazed at the black waters below them and shivered. The pale glimmer of whitecaps rolling across the windblown lake looked cold and foreboding.

"It's frightening out here at this time of night," she remarked.

He sounded amused. "There's nothing to be afraid of, Lisa."

She shifted and glanced at him. "After living in a jungle, I suppose this wouldn't seem frightening to you."

The corner of his mouth lifted a fraction. "After fighting the undergrowth, insects, and snakes—no." He flicked a glance at her. "One time I stepped on a constrictor as big as my leg."

"What did you do?"

He stared at the road and answered lightly, "I stepped off damn quickly."

She laughed, but then sobered, studying him. What had happened to him to make him so tough and strong? What had given him that air of savage ruthlessness?

They descended from the dam and turned along a narrow road that followed the east boundary of the lake. The asphalt was filled with potholes, crumbling along the edge.

"I've looked at this in the daylight," Clint said. "No one fishes on this side—it's full of rotting ancient docks.

It's noisy from this road, which is used mostly by trucks to get to warehouses in the area. The embankment's steep and rocky, making it difficult to reach the water to fish."

He paused a moment, then continued. "The city needs this artery desperately to carry traffic to the developing suburban areas. In the next few years, growth in this direction is expected to be tremendous."

His next question caught her off guard. "How come you weren't out with Tom tonight?"

"I . . . told him we shouldn't see each other any more. He has his story—that was what he wanted."

He looked at her closely but didn't say anything. After a quarter of a mile, Clint stopped and cut the motor, leaving the lights on. Their bright beams revealed dry red clay along the edge of the road, and yellowed grass and rocks.

He rested his hand on the door. "Want to get out and look?"

"I guess," she answered.

Clint picked up the map and stepped out. Lisa emerged into the cold. The rocky land sloped upwards from the road, then dropped away, out of sight. Just below this hill, a clump of oak trees spread to the water. Against the whitecaps, Lisa could see the end of a dock that jutted into the water.

Cold wind whipped at them, tearing Lisa's hair loose from the chignon. She turned her back against the biting chill.

Below them, waves crashed on the rocks with a steady rhythm. Clint's bulk loomed beside her, his black hair tangled by the wind. He seemed oblivious to the biting gusts or the low temperature.

"I'll show you where we are on this drawing and where the road could run."

Spreading the stiff, curling paper, he unfolded the map. The wind caught it and snatched it out of his hands.

He swore and lunged at it, as Lisa uttered a small cry of surprise.

The blowing paper was pale in the darkness. Clint bounded after it and caught it, but again the wind snapped it out of his fingers, rolling it over the rise of ground and out of sight.

Clint scrambled over the rocks and vanished into the darkness below. Lisa hurried to follow, slipped on a loose rock, and fell.

From below came the sound of Clint swearing, a tumbling of rocks, then a loud splash.

Lisa's heart lurched. She called his name, but the wind tore the sound away.

Unthinking, she scrambled up and sped blindly over the rise, unaware of slipping or catching herself against the sharp rocks.

Under her feet, small stones rolled away and clattered as they bounced down the slope. To her right, the wind whistled through a dark grove of trees, their thickness creating an impenetrable blackness.

She peered into the darkness, terrified that Clint had fallen into the lake.

"Clint!" she screamed. Without conscious thought Lisa rushed onto the dock, and felt the aged wood sag and sway from her momentum.

"Clint!" she called once more. From behind her, she heard his hoarse cry.

"Lisa, get off that damn dock!"

She whirled. The pressure of her running onto the rotten boards, together with the violent movement as she turned, was more than the dilapidated boards could withstand. The entire structure swayed crazily.

Her arms flailed in the air, and she leaped for the bank, but the dock fell away underneath her.

With a scream, Lisa tumbled into black, icy water.

chapter 16

THE SHOCK WAS bone-chilling. She opened her mouth to cry out and choked on weedy lake water. Consciousness faded; then, in a supreme effort, she fought against the freezing water.

Her limbs were constricted and dragged down by her heavy clothing. It was useless to struggle. She surrendered to numbing cold.

Something brushed her shoulder. Instantly arms closed like steel bands about her waist as blackness enveloped her.

She awoke to pain and a crushing weight. Clint was over her, trying to pump water from her lungs. His strong hands pushed against her back; dried twigs and pebbles scratched her face where it was pressed against the hard ground.

Gagging and coughing as she fought a wave of nausea, she cried aloud.

"Thank God!" Clint exclaimed, and rose, sweeping her into his arms.

Shivering violently against him and feeling that his body was as wet as hers, Lisa wrapped her arms around his neck. She shook so badly, it was impossible to talk.

Like daggers of ice, gusts of wind stabbed through her wet clothing. In long strides Clint reached the car and stopped at the back.

He set her on her feet, withdrew the car keys from his pocket, and unlocked the trunk of the car. Without a word he turned and yanked her coat away.

The movement startled her into speech. "What are you doing?" The words tumbled out in jerky gasps, as she huddled and quaked with cold.

He tossed the wet coat in the trunk. "You'll never get warm in all that wet clothing. Get out of it." Without hesitating, he unfastened her slacks and shoved them over her hips, ignoring her feeble protest.

Her hands were too numb and stiff to stop him. Her skin was pale against the darkness, her thin white shirt a bright blur.

Clint whipped out a blanket from the trunk and flung it over her. With lightning speed his own sweater went into the trunk, along with her clothing. The wet garments plopped with a splatter.

Lisa clutched the blanket, still shaking violently against the blasts of wind. Clint snatched it open to pull it around both of them.

He reached out a bare arm and slammed the trunk closed, then scooped her into his arms. "Hold the blanket," he commanded as he carried her to the car.

They squeezed behind the wheel; the motor roared, and Clint turned the heater on full blast.

Lisa wore only her soggy shirt and lacy underwear. She sat close to Clint, his denims wet against her legs, his chest bare against her shirt. Both of them shivered with cold; then Clint gradually became still.

Keeping one arm tightly around her, he drove with his free hand. The car roared along the road, its powerful motor gaining speed.

Underneath the blanket, heat radiated from Clint and in a moment Lisa began to absorb it.

With a squeal of tires, they rounded a curve. As warmth enveloped Lisa, the shock began to diminish; her awareness of Clint returned.

On another curve the car lurched crazily. "You could drive better if I moved out of your way," she murmured.

"Don't you move one damn inch," he commanded, so forcefully that she lapsed into silence.

They reached the expressway and turned in the opposite direction from which they had come. She stared at unfamiliar surroundings. "Are you taking me home?"

"My apartment is closer."

She glanced around in surprise. His face was just above hers, his firm jaw inches from her hair. They were quiet while the car sped along the deserted highway. After a moment Lisa felt his shoulders shaking.

She looked up and saw his teeth flash in a grin.

"Clint, you're laughing!"

A soft chuckle sounded in his throat. He kept his eyes on the road as he observed, "Lisa, you've developed a penchant for disaster."

Embarrassment swept over her. "You seem to bring out the worst in me!" she snapped.

The corners of his mouth widened. The more she listened to his soft chuckling, the angrier she became. It infuriated her to think of his laughing at her predicament.

"I guess the snow maiden has human moments after all," he stated mockingly.

She started to move away, but his arm tightened, holding her fast. "Ah, temper still!" His voice changed; the amusement disappeared as he looked down at her. "What happens, Lisa, if all that cold reserve melts away completely?"

"Let go of me, Clint!" she demanded. Because of her concern for him, she had fallen into the lake. His laughing at her for it made her seethe with anger.

There was a note of curiosity in his voice. "Why did you run out on that dock, Lisa? Were you afraid to be left alone?"

She looked up to find him gazing intently at her. His

black curls were plastered against his forehead; the gray eyes probed hers.

Her heart quickened. She had no intention of admitting what she felt and watching him laugh. "That's right," she answered.

"I was right there. I answered your call."

"I didn't hear you. I just heard a splash," she replied, then wished she hadn't revealed that much.

"I dislodged a rock, which rolled into the lake." His voice deepened. "Did you think I'd fallen in?"

Her cheeks burned, and she was thankful for the darkness. She looked down at the rough blue blanket. "I thought you might have." She shifted again to get away from him, embarrassed and irritated by his questions.

His arm tightened to pin her close. "You cared so much?"

She glanced at him quickly, then looked away. What a feeling of triumph he would have if she answered honestly, if she admitted how much she cared. What a laugh he would have over that, at her expense. She couldn't bear to have him do so, or to have him fling in her face his feelings for Eileen.

She let bitterness and anger creep into her voice. "Clint, if a dog had gone into those icy waters, I would have cared."

His jaw hardened. Lisa's heart turned over; then she shoved aside the regret. If she had answered any other way, he would have laughed at her even more.

Clint drove recklessly, in a stony silence. His speed climbed dangerously, but Lisa didn't comment.

She was aware of his eyes on her; she looked away to stare out the window. The warmer she became, the more conscious she grew of their bodies pressed close together. His arm held her tightly against his bare chest. Through the thin material of her shirt she could feel his steady, regular heartbeat.

Even more provocative was the feel of her bare legs

next to his, of the lean, hard muscles against her unclad thighs. The warmth was welcome; the touch of his naked flesh was not. It seared and burned into her skin, setting her on fire with longing, causing her to grow even more angry.

He slammed on the brakes, and the car rocked to a halt in front of an elegant apartment house. Fear washed through Lisa, a blind, consuming panic—not of Clint, but of her own desires. "Take me home, Clint," she begged.

"Don't be ridiculous. You need to get out of wet clothes and into warm ones as quickly as possible. Both of us do. Hold the blanket around us, Lisa, while I open the door."

His muscles tightened as he lifted her easily and stepped out. A cold gust of wind caught the loose ends of the blanket and tore away the warmth beneath it.

In long strides, Clint rushed to the door, while Lisa clutched the blanket. His arms were tight around her, his fingers splayed against her bare legs. Every touch sent a torrid message of awareness to her taut nerves.

She clung to him, conscious of the rippling muscles of his shoulders under her hands. They entered the darkened apartment; Clint kicked the door shut and set her on her feet.

The blanket slipped from her grasp. Lisa caught it up as he turned on the lights, but not swiftly enough to cover herself from his bold, raking glance.

The wet white shirt was molded to her body, outlining the full curves as if she wore nothing. Below it was only lacy underwear, her bare legs and feet.

She blushed hotly and swirled the blanket about her, receiving a sardonic look and lifted eyebrow from him.

"Ah, the snow maiden returneth," he murmured. He flipped the keys onto a marble-topped table near the entrance and grasped her arm firmly. "We've been together a lot, remember? Come on, this is a small bachelor apartment, and there's only one bathroom. You can have the first hot shower"—he paused, and a wicked gleam came in his eye—"unless you want to share it."

"That isn't funny, Clint!" she snapped, and attempted to jerk her arm free.

His fingers tightened; he answered in a drawl, "I never intended it to be."

As they moved through the apartment, Lisa saw that, while small, it was elegant down to the least detail, with thick Oriental carpets, original oil paintings, Louis XIV fruitwood-and-blue-velvet furniture.

She thought of the small apartment in which they had started their married life—gradually Clint had filled it with furniture he had made. She murmured, "Clint, where's the coffee table you made?"

"I got rid of all that, Lisa."

"Oh, no! I wish I'd known . . ."

He looked down at her. "What difference does it make? Why do you care?"

"I liked it," she replied.

She halted in the doorway of the bedroom while he flipped a switch, and soft light flooded the room. At the sight of the oversized bed beneath a tiger-stripe fur spread, Lisa sucked in her breath. The imposing bed had an ornate carved headboard with a long mirror inserted in the center of the dark, burnished walnut. Across from the bed was a wide brick fireplace.

"Is this your love nest?" she snapped impulsively. Immediately she blushed and wished she hadn't spoken.

His mocking gray eyes held hers. "Scared to enter?"

She raised her chin and walked into the room. "No."

He laughed softly, and she blushed at the amusement reflected in his eyes. He raised his hand to point. "There's the bathroom. Get in there and take a hot shower—it will be the best way to combat the chill. I'll find some dry clothes for you and bring them in. You'll find a hair dryer too."

Aware of her reflection in a long mirror that covered a section of the wall, she crossed the room. Her hair had come unpinned and hung in long, wet straggles around her face. Her make-up was washed away, and she peered out of the blanket with wide blue eyes filled with trepidation.

She faced him. "As soon as I get dry, Clint, will you take me home?"

"Of course," he replied with derision. "I wouldn't dream of holding you here against your will, Lisa."

Something about his tone wasn't the least reassuring; his eyes danced with mocking amusement. If she weren't careful and away from Clint soon, tonight would merely be another painful episode.

Lisa swept into the bathroom and locked the door, thankful to be out of his disturbing presence. The bathroom was as sensually decorated as the bedroom. An entire wall was covered with mirrors. Everywhere she turned she glimpsed her reflection. Traces of Clint's after-shave hung in the air; Lisa felt as if his presence permeated every nook and cranny of the apartment, everything he possessed.

She dropped the blanket in a heap and shivered even in the warmth of the cozy room. As she peeled off her underwear, she sneezed violently several times.

Once in the shower, hot water warmed her thoroughly. Finally she stepped out and wrapped herself in a thick brown towel.

A knock sounded; Clint announced, "I have some dry clothes, Lisa."

She unlocked the door, and Clint handed her a black satin robe. He regarded her intently, then merely turned away. Lisa shut the door.

She dried her hair quickly, using his brush to smooth the long strands until they fell in a silky sheen below her shoulders. She removed the towel and slipped into the black satin robe.

Her mouth firmed as she discovered there were no fastenings except for a satin belt. From the size, it was undoubtedly Clint's; she wrapped its voluminous folds about her body, pulled the collar high, and tied the belt.

She stared at her reflection. Golden hair framed her face, which was pale with no make-up; her lips were rosy. The black satin clung to her body, revealing the curves of her breasts and her long, slender legs.

Damn Clint anyway, she thought, for giving her something so revealing and sexy to wear. She pulled the collar higher, until it was under her ears, then opened the door.

She stopped at the sight of a fire burning in the fireplace, the dim lighting, and the sound of music playing softly. Clint turned from the closet with a handful of clothing.

His eyes went over her slowly, from head to toe, like a caress instead of an observation, lingering on each curve, every slim line, until she burned with embarrassment.

She motioned toward the bathroom and the pile of wet clothing. "Clint, do you have a clothes dryer?"

"Sorry, I send it all out."

She gazed at him in dismay. "I can't wear this home!"

He shrugged indifferently. "I'll hang them over one of the heating outlets."

"It will take a week to dry my things."

"Lisa, can we discuss this after my shower? I'm still cold and wet."

She looked at him in surprise. "I'm sorry," she apologized quickly.

He motioned with his hand, dismissing her apology. "There's a glass of brandy on the table. Drink it, because it will warm you thoroughly."

"No, thanks."

His head came up and he regarded her with speculation. "Still afraid you'll let down your defenses, aren't you?"

"No!" She was tired of his baiting. She marched defiantly to the table and gulped down the brandy, then set the glass down with a click and faced him.

He appeared to be biting back a laugh, and she suddenly felt foolish for her show of false bravado. The intimacy of the moment dawned on her—Clint's getting his clean clothes out of the closet while she waited, dressed only in a satin robe—and, worst of all, the indecent bedroom, with the overpowering bed.

She wanted to escape from all of it. She stared at him as he rummaged in the closet. His back was to her, the broad shoulders tapering to a slim waist, while the muscles rippled as he reached for a shirt.

Before she could do anything, he turned and motioned toward the bed. "Have you ever slept on a water bed, Lisa?" He laughed softly. "I already know the answer. I'm sure you haven't. That would be far beneath your dignity." His eyes danced wickedly with amusement. "Once I broke down that dignified reserve, didn't I?" He waved his hand in the direction of the bed. "Go ahead and try it."

"No, thanks, Clint," she replied stiffly.

She felt he was laughing at her again. His voice was teasing. "Lisa, you'll be perfectly safe. You'll have the room to yourself. The moment you hear my shower stop running, you can jump off the bed."

He picked up a brush and moved toward the bathroom, with the folded clothing in his hand. "Go on; you'll be in here alone, and I won't bother you."

As he neared, he paused to pick up the crystal decanter of amber brandy; two glasses were next to it. He refilled hers, then poured one for himself.

He faced her, holding his clothes and the glass of brandy. His cool gaze swept over her. "You ought to thaw a little, Lisa. Life could be a lot more fun."

She stared at his bare chest, with its black hair curling against brown skin, and thought again how much he had changed. A white scar ran along his ribs. She raised her eyes and met his.

"Another fight?" she asked.

Aware of her scrutiny, he looked down. "Yes, a knife fight that time." A ruthless look appeared in his eyes, making his features harsh. "I had a bit of growing up to do myself." The piercing gray eyes bore into hers. "I don't regret it."

"Clint, will you shower, so you can take me home?" His presence was overwhelming. The fire threw dancing shadows across the dimly lighted room. She could feel the tension between them; the charged atmosphere grew more taut with every passing second.

Slowly, insolently, his mocking eyes perused her, then raised to meet her gaze. "I can see your heart beating against the fabric of the dressing gown, Lisa. Why is it so fast?"

Her cheeks burned, and she fought against the impulse to glance down at her breast to see if the fluttering pulse was revealed—or if Clint were merely taunting her. Her gaze flickered around him.

Without seeming to, he had stopped so that he was blocking her from moving away unless he stepped aside. She felt trapped and frightened.

To avoid his question, she sipped brandy and looked at him. "You've changed so much, Clint; what caused it?"

A sardonic glint shone in his eye, as if he knew her question was a ploy to avoid answering his own. Before he replied, he drank some of his brandy.

"A lot of things have caused me to change, Lisa. Hard physical labor, having to cope with responsibility for a road crew when we were buried in a jungle hundreds of miles from any kind of civilization. To live with jaguars, parrots, and bushmasters, tending to injured men the best I could."

Reaching out, he placed his hand at the back of her

neck. He moved his fingers lightly in her hair. "When I first went down there, it was hell. I was in primitive places, working fourteen to fifteen hours a day, in a steaming tropical rain forest, doing hard labor, staying in squalid villages, getting drunk and into fights. I held on to my sanity by thinking about you, about my cool, lovely wife."

At the touch of his warm hand, electricity coursed through her. Overwhelmed by the contact, by his piercing gray eyes, and by his nearness, she remained still.

"You've changed, too, Lisa—and have not changed at the same time. You still seem untouched—as much a virgin as you were on our wedding night." His voice dropped to an intimate huskiness. "Yet I know you're not." After a moment, he frowned.

"I was dumbfounded, Lisa, when you told me about the offer Dad made to you to get a divorce—and that you didn't accept it."

"Did you think I wanted your money?" she asked with a laugh.

He shook his head. "No. I wondered about many things between us, but that wasn't one of them. You're too fiercely independent. I could have saved Dad some trouble if he'd asked me first."

She gazed at him, at the dark lashes and crooked nose. She longed to deny his statement, to tell him she was not so independent as she had thought, that she needed him. But it would be futile to do so.

With a bold stare that made Lisa feel stripped naked, his gray eyes raked slowly down the length of her body.

She stirred uncomfortably. "Clint..." It was difficult to speak, and even though she shifted slightly, his hand remained against the back of her neck.

"You're frightened of me, Lisa."

She stared up at him as silence stretched between them. She could not summon any words; all rational thought left her. She struggled against the feelings he stirred.

His voice was like soft velvet. "Or are you frightened of something else?"

She would be hopelessly lost if she didn't make him stop. Lisa wrenched away, stepping backwards and bumping into the table, causing her brandy to slosh and the decanter on the table to rock.

Clint reached around her quickly and straightened the bottle. She was aware of his bare chest, inches from her face, as he straightened slowly.

"I'm not afraid, Clint," she said with an effort.

He laughed softly and caught her chin in his fingers. "Oh, yes, you are." His eyes dropped to her breast. "Look at your heartbeat, Lisa."

"Clint..." In desperation she snapped, "If I'm afraid, it's because I don't know what you'll do next!"

His gaze mocked her. "Oh, no, Lisa. You're afraid because of exactly what you expect me to do next! Can you trust yourself at all?"

"That's ridiculous!" she exclaimed, while all the time her wildly beating pulse, her breathlessness, and raw awareness of his body silently proclaimed the validity of his words.

"Ridiculous," he mimicked. "Let's see if you can prove it, Lisa." His dark eyebrow climbed, giving him a devilish look. "Give me a kiss."

"No!" she blurted out, more forcefully than she'd intended.

He chuckled softly. "You're scared to death. You can't trust yourself in the least."

He started to turn away. A flash of anger rippled through Lisa. She reached out swiftly and grasped his arm.

Instantly he whirled around, his eyes narrowed.

"I'm not scared of my own feelings, Clint," she said

in a low, angry voice. "I'm frightened of your brute force, your ruthless will."

All amusement was gone from his face. His voice was low and filled with challenge. "I don't believe you." He spoke tensely. "Come kiss me, Lisa. I won't move a muscle."

She stared at him, feeling lost in the depths of his gray eyes. "And have you go back on your word? No, thank you." She brushed past him, fighting to keep her voice level.

Every nerve in her back tingled as she crossed to the fire and stared at the burning logs. It was an effort not to turn around to look at him. After a moment she couldn't resist the temptation.

She turned slowly and gazed at an empty room. Clint had stepped into the bathroom and closed the door.

She lifted the glass of brandy and drank deeply, feeling the hot liquid curl through her, as burning as her feelings kindled by Clint's smoldering glances.

Clint was right. She was terrified of her own reaction to him. She looked down at the smooth black satin and saw the steady rise and fall of her breast.

Had he actually been able to tell her pulse was beating faster? Or was it a taunting exaggeration? There was no question that it did beat more quickly; she only wondered whether he could discern it by looking at her. Lisa knew all Clint had to do was enter the room once again, and it would race just as fast as it had before.

She stared at the room, which proclaimed "male" and "sex" in its every decoration, every piece of furniture. The oversized bed dominated; she wondered if Eileen had shared this room with Clint.

All too easily she could envision Eileen's voluptuous body, the flaming hair against the fur spread. Lisa whirled and stared into the fire, finishing the glass of brandy.

Determinedly, she promised herself that as soon as Clint emerged from the shower, she would insist on returning home. She had to escape from his presence, from this room, from her own response to him.

Gradually the combination of brandy and the warmth of the fire relaxed Lisa's raw nerves. She glanced at the bed, tempted to stretch out until Clint returned.

Through the closed bathroom door a rush of drumming water sounded. As she strolled around the room, which was so clearly meant for intimate moments, with its dim lights, music, and the cozy fire, she debated whether to try the bed.

The reassuring noise of the shower continued. Lisa crossed to punch the bed lightly, making a small ripple underneath the fur spread.

She placed the brandy glass on a table and sat down on the bed. It undulated gently under her weight. She moved to the middle and fell backwards, rocking up and down.

Staring at the ceiling while the motion gradually subsided, she lay still. The steady rise and fall of the bed, the warmth of the room, the brandy, lulled Lisa to sleep. She drifted off, unaware of doing so until, later, she opened her eyes.

She blinked. Directly in front of her face was a lean bare arm.

Clint sat beside her, with an arm on either side of her head. She lay on her side, the black satin robe partially open, exposing the soft curve of a creamy breast.

She glanced down and discovered the folds had fallen back to reveal a bare thigh and knee.

She blushed and yanked the robe tight, staring up at Clint. He wore a short-sleeved black robe; its darkness lent him an air of ruthlessness.

His black hair was washed; with dark highlights, it gleamed and curled against his neck. A faint trace of musk after-shave mingled with the clean smell of lemon soap. The robe was partially open, revealing his bare chest.

For an instant Lisa couldn't get her breath. She fought to speak in a calm voice. "Get away, Clint."

"You're very beautiful."

"You said I'd be alone," she whispered.

"You were," he replied in a voice that was like a caress. "I never promised anything after I finished my shower."

"Don't touch me, Clint." She hoped he couldn't hear her pounding heart. She lay under his gaze, which moved slowly along the length of her body.

Lisa caught her breath. Desire curled and flamed deep within her. Supine, a knee slightly bent, an arm flung to one side, her hair fanned behind her head, she did not move a muscle, but lay still, appearing relaxed. Inside, she had never felt so tense. It was as if all her nerves were on little wires that had been wound as tightly as possible. The smallest twist and they would break, to fly apart in a thousand directions.

And she would lose all control.

Clint's eyes were smoldering and intent. "I thought you were in love with Tom Perkins."

She turned her head to one side. "No."

"Were you ever?"

She glanced at him. The thick black lashes did not hide his piercing look. She shook her head slightly. "Never."

"You weren't in love with me when I returned from Peru," he stated.

She stared up at his harsh features and wanted to reply that she had been in love with him since their very first date. Instead, she answered, "I just met Tom the day you returned. I told you, Clint, that he wanted a story. He hopes to get another job, and the articles about me helped."

"Lisa"—his silvery-gray eyes possessed hers—"I wanted you to go to Peru with me, you know that. All the time I was down there, I dreamed of you. I think that's why I had so many fights—I was in a murderous mood."

Every second that ticked by was to her disadvantage. The conversation was not as devastating as his presence. "Let me up, Clint," she demanded.

She met his fiery gaze; his voice was hoarse as he asked, "Lisa, why did you run out on that dock tonight?"

With a cry she rolled away in an attempt to escape his probing stare. She tumbled against his arm, which was like hitting a trunk of solid oak; he remained rigid, preventing her from breaking free.

Clint caught her up in his arms and forced her to face him. "Answer my question, Lisa."

She squeezed her eyes shut tightly; her head rocked to and fro on her slender neck, while the long hair swung with each movement. Like spun silk, its golden strands caught the light.

He shook her gently. "Answer me," he commanded.

She faced him and refused. "No!"

He crushed her to him, his mouth moving on hers, forcing hers open. Lisa fought, like a caged animal with an instinct for self-preservation, against her own passion.

His arms tightened. In a second she felt cool air against her bare shoulders. The robe tumbled around her waist—Clint's was gone. The thick curling hair on his chest tickled her flesh.

She moaned in exquisite torment; her struggles ceased, changed to responses. As if flood gates had been opened, all the passion, the yearning she had so carefully held in check, burst free.

Clint raised his head; his gray eyes ravished her slender naked body. His hands were everywhere, with light caresses that set her on fire.

With a harsh cry that died deep in her throat, she

began to move against him, to writhe with desire that rose to a frenzy.

The waterbed rocked violently under their movements until suddenly Clint stood up. In a sweeping movement he placed her on her feet beside him, with his arm around her; with the other hand he caught the fur spread and flung it to the floor in front of the fire, then scooped her up to carry her to it.

Lisa made one last attempt to stop him. "Clint, please, no . . ."

Gently, he lowered her and stretched his full length to pull her against his hard, lean body. He kissed her throat, the hollows of her neck; his lips were warm, his tongue burning, provoking an instant response from her.

"All that cold reserve wasn't really you," he murmured, kissing her continually, "and now it's finally gone . . ."

"Stop, Clint . . ." she cried softly, but her arms disputed her words. She clung to him; her fingers moved over the tough, hard muscles, into the thick waving hair that curled along his neck.

Her body molded to his; her flesh was a pale contrast to his.

His hand moved along her back, caressing the smooth skin, shifting lower until she was wild with desire, until all thought and logic fled.

Lisa was aware of nothing but Clint. Her world diminished to his strong arms and his hard, male body.

Drowned in passion, she yielded to him. Giving fully, Lisa lost all reserve. The love she felt for Clint began to pour forth.

Their arms entwined as they consummated the feverish desire that flared like the fire in the hearth.

chapter 17

CLINT LAY STILL, one brown arm beneath her shoulders; the other lay across her smooth bare waist. Softly, against her ear, he murmured endearments.

Lisa closed her eyes. She was swamped with grief. She lay perfectly still, as if asleep. Clint was attracted to Eileen. There had been the South American actress. . . . No one woman was the world to Clint, as he was to her.

Finally he became quiet. He pulled her closer into his arms; then his breathing became deep and regular.

Hot tears coursed down Lisa's cheeks. She slipped carefully away from him.

For an instant she leaned over him, her eyes sweeping the long, powerful body, memorizing every detail of Clint until she could not see for her tears.

She had to get away; she didn't want another confrontation. Shamelessly, in spite of the fact that she knew he was seeking a divorce, that he might be having an affair with Eileen, she had let him do all he wanted. Not only allowed him to, but had begged him to.

She rose, then looked around in dismay. She had nothing to wear home. Some of her wet things were still locked in the trunk of Clint's car.

She crossed to the closet and snatched a heavy black topcoat off a hanger. She wrapped herself in it, swallowed up by the size but assured that the bulky garment covered her nakedness.

She had to have something for her bare feet. Her own shoes must have gone into the lake. Finally she selected a pair of Clint's western boots and pulled them on.

Once more she glanced at Clint as he lay sleeping in front of the fire, his long body like a Grecian statue.

The longing to place her hand against his cheek, to caress the hard bronze skin, was overwhelming. Quickly, she turned away.

Walking with difficulty in the oversized boots, she tiptoed to the door. She closed the bedroom door without a sound, then rushed across the living room as if the devil were after her—the devilish desire of her own body for Clint.

The boots clacked on the entryway floor. She stepped outside into sleet. For an instant, Lisa paused and blinked with surprise, then hurried on.

Sharp pellets of ice stung her cheeks, and she bent her head against their chill. She turned the collar of the coat high and pulled it up around her face.

She hurried away from the apartment, down the walk toward the street, a solitary figure hunched against the storm.

Suddenly she heard her name. "Lisa!"

She glanced over her shoulder. Clint charged out of the apartment after her, leaving the door open in his haste.

He yanked on his parka as he closed the space between them in long strides.

She turned to run, but he caught her easily and spun her around to face him.

He had pulled on tight jeans under the parka. When he spoke, his voice was a rasp. "What the hell are you doing?"

Tears streamed down her cheeks; she squeezed her eyes shut. "Let go of me, Clint. You got what you wanted; now leave me alone."

"Lisa, you'll get pneumonia out here! Get back inside!"

"No!" she screamed at him, and wrenched her arm from his grasp. She faced him squarely. "Stop tormenting me, Clint!"

They stared at each other. "Let me take you home," he said quietly.

"No! I don't want to ride with you! I don't want to be in your apartment!" Lisa shouted. "Just go away and leave me alone!"

His eyes narrowed, and his hand closed in a viselike grip on her shoulder, pinching her flesh until she gasped.

His voice was a rasp. "All right, Lisa, I'll leave you be—if you'll answer one question honestly."

She bit back a cry at the pain from his fingers. "What is it?"

"You never did tell me. Why did you run onto that dock tonight?"

She raised her chin and met his intent stare. "You don't leave me any pride, do you, Clint?" In the large sleeves of his coat she clenched her fists tightly. "I suppose you have a right to revenge for the way I treated you when you came home from Peru." The words rushed out. She jerked free and backed away from him. "I ran out there because I was afraid you'd fallen into the lake!"

She took another step backwards and cried, "There! Does that make you satisfied? You can take that information and gloat over it when you make love to Eileen!" She felt a wave of hysteria. "I know it serves me right . . ."

Lisa whirled and ran, then stumbled in the large boots.

Strong arms caught her. She could no longer control her feelings. She struggled, screaming at him as she flailed with her fists. "You promised you would leave me alone! Let me go!"

Her blond hair swirled about her shoulders as she

attempted to break free of his grasp. "I admitted it. You have your pound of flesh! Now keep your word and let me go!"

She felt defenseless against his brute strength, against his arrogance. He spoke above the noise of the sleet and driving wind.

"Lisa, I haven't made love to Eileen." He leaned closer to peer at her.

She looked up at him in surprise. "She doesn't mean anything to you?"

He frowned. "Why the devil would she? She's the one who had that article put in *The Press*—"

Lisa interrupted in surprise. "Why did she do that?"

For an instant he frowned. "Because she thought it would accomplish just what it did—we had a fight about it."

Bewilderment filled Lisa. She gazed at him, perplexed. "You were at the banquet with her. She's going to work for you . . ."

He cut her words short. "Lisa, I told you that night at the banquet, I was there to see you get that award. It was the only way I could do so. Eileen isn't going to work for me. She applied and was turned down. I have enough complications in my life without hiring employees like Eileen."

He slid his hands over her shoulders and turned up the collar of her coat under her chin. "Lisa, I brought her along when you were stranded because I honestly thought you wouldn't want to be alone with me, and she was the only friend of yours I knew. I was introduced to her as your friend—remember?"

"I thought you might be falling in love with her," Lisa stated dazedly.

His voice was earnest. "Lisa, after being married to you, how could I want someone like Eileen?"

She frowned. "Oh, Clint, Eileen is sexy and beautiful

and worships you. Clint"—she bit her lip—"she told me she would marry you when you get the divorce."

He swore softly. "When did she tell you that?"

Wind whipped her hair; pale strands blew across Clint's shoulders. It tore her words away as she looked up into his face. "At the banquet," she answered. Suddenly she sneezed.

He frowned at her and glanced around. "You're going to get pneumonia. Come here."

She stared up at his face, the harsh features, black curls tossed by the wind. Gray scudding clouds etched his dark hair and wide shoulders. He stepped closer and swung her easily into his arms.

His boots crunched on small pellets of sleet as he headed for the apartment. The parking lot and street were deserted. Clint's tall figure, carrying Lisa effortlessly, moved swiftly through the night.

It was impossible to talk as he crossed the ground in long strides. Lisa clung to him and buried her head against the warmth of his neck, while thoughts of all he had told her ran through her mind.

In the entryway, where he had left the door open, sleet had fallen, and tiny drops of water sparkled. The hall was cold. Clint kicked the door shut behind him.

Without hesitating, he moved through the living room to the bedroom, close to the fire. Using his toe, he tugged a large leather chair close to the hearth.

Holding Lisa tightly, Clint sat down. He reached up and took her chin to turn her to face him. Solemnly, he asked, "Lisa, why didn't we sit down and talk like this sooner? We've caused each other a lot of unnecessary heartache."

She met his gaze and took a deep breath. "Clint, I grew up learning to bottle up my feelings, to keep everything to myself. Just because you exchange marriage vows doesn't mean you can change all your ways."

His hands closed over hers. "Lisa, Eileen was no friend. I haven't been falling in love with her." She looked at him soberly and remained silent, while he said, "There's only one person I truly love." He placed his hands on both sides of her face. "I think there is something overdue here. I love you, Lisa."

Her heart leaped. "Oh, Clint!" She looked at him wonderingly.

"I think, Lisa," he said dryly, "if we'd both learned to speak out honestly and say what we felt, we could have saved ourselves a great deal of trouble."

Her pulse quickened. Disbelief and amazement coursed through her. "Clint, you told me you were going to call a lawyer about a divorce. . . ."

"I was angry over that article. I thought you were considering having an affair with Tom Perkins. . . . That night when I brought you home from Seiling, I wanted to punch him right in the nose when he put his arms around you."

She gazed at him solemnly. "Then you can understand how I felt about Eileen." Lisa ran her hands over his wrists, feeling the hard bones. "That was agony, Clint, to watch her touch you and flirt with you all the time."

He looked surprised. "You didn't give any indication that it mattered." He paused, then added, "I didn't notice Eileen very much. You'll never know how worried I was about you." He laughed. "I couldn't keep my eyes off the mirror to look at you, until you scooted across the seat."

"I found those looks too disturbing," she admitted, "but I didn't guess the reason for them."

"Lisa, if it was agony to see Eileen flirt with me, that must mean you care. Why didn't you tell me?"

She looked at the fire. "I wanted to, Clint. I even started to, then several things happened."

"What?"

She turned her hands before the glowing embers. A log crackled and popped. "I was going to the day you took me to lunch, but you walked out with Eileen, and she kissed you. . . ."

He groaned. "Lisa, in the first place, she kissed me— I didn't kiss her. In the second place, do you know what a kiss means to a girl like Eileen?"

She glanced at him. "Well, maybe not much. . ."

"How many men have you seen her kiss around your office?"

"That's true, but it looked as if you were in love with her."

"Honey, it meant nothing. Maybe I allowed her to because you were always so cold and aloof and Perkins was always hovering in the background."

Lisa sighed and kept her eyes downcast. "Clint, I don't know why you didn't see the effect you had on me every time you were near."

"The effect!" He shifted impatiently and looked at her with narrowed eyes. "You've been angry as the devil with me every time I came close."

"Maybe I was just trying to hide my feelings, Clint. I lose my train of thought when I'm near you." She faced him. "That wasn't the only reason I didn't tell you."

"Why else?"

Lisa looked into his eyes. "Clint, none of this was necessary. If you had really loved me and wanted me back, all you had to do was tell me that you weren't returning to Peru." She tilted her head to one side to look at him. "Why didn't you?"

He took her hands, then glanced down at them. "You're still cold. Wait a minute while I build up the fire." He lifted her and placed her in the chair, then moved to fetch a log. While he worked, he answered her. "Lisa, I did try to explain, but you wouldn't listen. When I came back from Peru, I wasn't president. I wasn't wanted here by the men who were running the company. Dad always liked to do things his own way. I knew he was unhappy about our marriage, but I didn't realize the extent of his feelings." He squatted in front of the fire and carefully placed more logs over the hot embers. When he straightened, he slipped off the parka, leaving his chest bare above tight, faded jeans.

Clint poked the logs and continued, "Dad sent me to Peru. He may have hoped to wreck our marriage. When I returned, everything was in a mess; the people in charge didn't want me to take over. Fortunately, there were some who knew what I had done in South America and thought I could manage here. They were willing to back me. For a time I wasn't certain if we could keep the company alive."

He replaced the poker, then turned to look down at her. He put his hands on his hips. "I didn't want to come home and tell you I was taking over and staying, when it might not be true."

"You could have said there was a possibility," she stated quietly.

"If you will recall, at our first encounter you were very aloof, Lisa. Also, you told me you had to get home for a date. Suddenly I didn't know where I stood. You walked out on me when I had to go to Peru. You didn't answer my letters..." When she started to speak, he said, "I know—the South American actress. I told you she meant nothing."

"But when you knew there was a possibility you might take over and stay—"

"Lisa," he interrupted her, "when I returned, I didn't know what I was coming back to. One of the men had cabled me that we were getting ready to liquidate the company. I had to wind things up in Peru. I came home for Dad's funeral, then went back to help train someone to take over for me so I could come home. I didn't know if there would even *be* a company, much less if I would stay here."

He shifted his weight and said, "We made changes in a hurry. I became president and I intended to tell you, but then Perkins dropped that little bomb in his article and you saw it there." He looked at her.

In a few seconds he added, "It might not have been wise, Lisa, but deep down I think there was one more reason I didn't walk right in and tell you."

"What was it, Clint?"

"I wanted you to want me as badly as I wanted you. I hoped that you would want me and need me more than a career or a job or any other damn thing..."

Lisa's heart felt as if it would burst with joy. "Oh, Clint, I've wanted you so badly..."

He took a step and reached down to take her hand and pull her up into his arms. He gazed at her solemnly. "I love you, Lisa." Suddenly he groaned and crushed her to him while he leaned down to kiss her hungrily.

Joy, love, and longing coursed through Lisa. She returned his kiss wildly, trying to convey her feelings to him.

Finally he released her slightly. Lisa looked up at him. "Clint, I should have gone with you. At the time I felt it was unfair to ask me to give up my career just when I was getting started. It was important to me to prove that I could do something on my own."

"That damned independence," he growled. "That independence, and thinking you had to live up to your family..."

"Clint, my family, you—all had been successful. I had never done anything, and I just had to try...."

"Well, you succeeded," he stated dryly.

"It wasn't worth it," she whispered.

He tilted her chin up to search her face. "Do you mean that?"

She looked at him solemnly and told him, "Clint, I should never have walked out. I should have stayed with you . . ."

"That's all behind us now," he murmured. "You may have been right in what you did, Lisa."

"I missed you so much," she whispered. "I tried to forget you. I'd even convinced myself that I had—until the first five minutes you were back . . ."

His gray eyes clouded. "Why didn't you tell me then?"

"I was afraid of being hurt again. Then everything was tangled up, with Eileen, and the lake . . ."

"Oh, Lisa," he breathed softly, and pulled her to him. His kiss was tender, filled with love, with a promise of passion. His arms tightened, and he held her closer. His voice was husky. "I love you, I love you. I'll say it every minute if you like."

She looked up at him. "I'll settle for once every hour."

He smiled. "Thank goodness the wind blew that map out of my hand tonight."

"Did you ever get it back?"

He shook his head. "I lost it when I went into the lake after you. It wasn't that important." He caught the heavy strands of her hair in both his hands and looked at her uptilted face. "I couldn't believe you'd run out there. That was very heroic, Lisa."

She laughed. "I didn't stop to think about heroics."

He remained solemn. "I mean it, honey. I think I recall accusing you of being too fearful, only a short time before that, when we were crossing the dam."

"It didn't bother me, Clint."

His voice was soft. "I take it all back. Not only are you brave enough to stand up to my temper, but you dash out on a crumbling dock over icy waters to save me from drowning. If you hadn't gone into the lake, we would still be at cross purposes."

The corners of his mouth twitched slightly, as if he

were fighting down a smile. "I couldn't believe it when I saw you run out there and call my name." Laughter bubbled up in his throat. "Not much more than I could believe my eyes when I ran out of the apartment a while ago and saw you trudging away in my topcoat and boots."

Her face flamed as she remembered the way she looked. She clutched the coat collar around her chin. "I had to find something to wear home. I lost my shoes, and my coat must still be locked in the trunk of your car."

His warm fingers reached out and closed over hers, lifting hers away so he could unbutton the topcoat.

"You don't have anything on under that, Lisa, do you?"

It was difficult to speak. She felt as if she were drowning in his gray eyes. The thick black lashes drooped over them, and all amusement left his face.

He stared at her. His gaze was torrid and filled with yearning.

Flaming desire raced through Lisa. She was consumed by his hungry look. She wanted the long, hard body to possess her again.

"Nothing," she whispered, aware that his fingers were deliberately unfastening each button until he shoved open the coat and it slid to the floor.

With her gaze held captive by his, she stepped out of the boots.

Effortlessly, Clint lifted her in his arms. Lisa clung to him, filled with love for him, wild with longing for him. He lowered her to the fur spread and stretched out beside her.

Soft light from the fire bathed them, tinting her pale skin pink. She lay on the fur spread, the stiff tiger-hair prickly against her back. Her golden hair fanned out around her head.

She placed her hands on Clint's broad shoulders. He

raised himself on one hand and gazed down at her. "We'll get our own home, Lisa. You can have whatever you want. Someday I intend to take you to see Peru."

"Clint, I can't oppose you at the hearing," she whispered.

He placed his finger against her lips to silence her. "We can work together to present that alternate route."

He bent and kissed her throat; his mouth moved hungrily to her lips while his hands explored her body, causing wave after wave of desire to wash over her.

Lisa fitted herself into his shoulder, turning as he shifted and stretched the length of her; his weight came down on her.

She clung to the powerful shoulders and returned kiss for kiss, returned his caresses, relishing the feel of his skin, his hard legs and arms.

The crackle of logs, an occasional pop of an ember, were the only sounds in the room; the glowing fire bathed their skin in warm light.

Clint paused and said huskily, "I'm glad some of your clothes are at the bottom of the lake. I intend to burn the rest. We have a lot of lost time to make up for."

He kissed her temple, her cheek; his lips lightly brushed her mouth, causing a tingling that made Lisa turn to kiss him eagerly.

"I don't intend to let you out of this apartment for weeks." He whispered in her ear, "You can forget about clothes, Mrs. Callaway. I may not let you cover that body until the spring thaw."

"I think your arrogance is showing again, Mr. Callaway," she murmured in a teasing voice. She wrapped her arms around his neck and gazed up at him.

chapter 18

THE HOTEL ROOM was quiet, dim in the light of early morning that poured through the floor-to-ceiling glass doors. Lisa gazed outside at the rugged crags of the Andes Mountains in the distance. She shifted and felt Clint's arm tighten around her shoulders. Stirring languorously, she gazed at her husband stretched out beside her.

"Clint." She spoke softly.

"Hmmm?" He rolled over to look at her and smiled.

"Clint, it seems absurd to spend all that money to fly to Peru for just a week. It's even more ridiculous never to leave this hotel room."

His voice was warm and husky. "You don't like this?"

She laughed and wound her arms around his neck. "What do you think?" She lifted her mouth to his.

His kiss was filled with love and tenderness, different from the fiery kisses of an hour earlier. When he released her, he sat up in bed.

The sheet fell casually across his bare stomach, and Lisa retrieved a filmy peignoir from the floor. She slipped it on while Clint talked.

"Today, I promise, Lisa, we'll see Machu Picchu, home of the Incas."

"Uh huh, Clint."

He chuckled. "I have a proposition to make you, Mrs. Callaway." He wrapped his arm around her shoulders.

"I mentioned once that I'd like to have you start a house organ for Callaway. The offer is still open."

She giggled. "This is the first job interview I've ever had in bed!"

With a mocking leer he pushed open the peignoir. "I'd say you're abundantly qualified."

"Clint!" She tugged the folds of material together and laughed at him. He gazed down at her contentedly.

"I do mean it, Lisa. If you want the job—it's yours. We need a trade journal to help tie the organization together. With offices strung out in the United States and South America, a journal would help unify the employees."

She studied him solemnly. "Do you think we could work together, Clint?"

"I wouldn't have offered you the job if I didn't think so." A teasing note had entered his voice. "There are many fringe benefits."

"I'm sure!" She ran her hand along his strong brown arm, feeling the stiff black hairs brush her finger. "I make a nice salary in my present job, Clint."

"I'd match it," he answered casually.

"You don't even know how much it is."

He kissed her temple. "I'd still match it to get you."

She straightened and twisted to face him. "Why?"

His gray eyes gazed at her with an unwavering directness. "Lisa, I'm going to pull that company out of trouble. I'm surrounding myself with good people. I know you're capable and would get the job done."

She looked at him thoughtfully. "What would happen, Clint, when we disagreed?"

"We'd settle it some way."

"Clint, I've worked for a nice, mild man, who's never raised his voice the whole time I've been employed."

His white teeth flashed in a wicked grin. "It's time you had a challenge."

She considered his offer. It would be exciting to work

with Clint, to start a journal and be in charge of it. "Are you sure you'd want to see that much of me—day and night?"

His arm slipped around her waist, and he leaned forward to kiss her with deliberate thoroughness. Then he looked at her. "Now what do you think?"

"I'm tempted to accept, Clint."

"Good." He smiled. "Come on. We'll go look at Peru."

She slipped out of bed to dress. The thick carpet was soft against her bare feet, and the gossamer peignoir brushed lightly against her ankles. She rummaged in the open suitcase for lacy underwear, then turned toward the bathroom. She glanced at Clint.

Still sitting in bed, he gazed at her with smoldering eyes. His voice had a throaty roughness. "Come here a minute, honey."

She laughed. "Now, Clint . . ."

With a lithe movement he slid across the bed and rose. The sheet fell away from his trim, muscled body, and all laughter died in her throat. He reached for her and drew her into his arms. His gray eyes darkened, and he leaned forward to kiss her.

He paused and whispered, "I swear, Lisa, we'll see Machu Picchu tomorrow . . ."

She locked her arms around his neck, relishing the feeling of his strong, hard length. Through half-closed eyes, she murmured happily, "I don't care, Clint. I can wait. . . ."

QUESTIONNAIRE

1. How many romances do you *read* each month? _____

2. How many of these do you *buy* each month? _____

3. Do you read primarily
   - ☐ novels in romance lines like SECOND CHANCE AT LOVE
   - ☐ historical romances
   - ☐ bestselling contemporary romances
   - ☐ other _____

4. Were the love scenes in this novel (this is book # _____)
   - ☐ too explicit
   - ☐ not explicit enough
   - ☐ tastefully handled

5. On what basis do you make your decision to buy a romance?
   - ☐ friend's recommendation
   - ☐ bookseller's recommendation
   - ☐ art on the front cover
   - ☐ description of the plot on the back cover
   - ☐ author
   - ☐ other _____

6. Where did you buy this book?
   - ☐ chain store (drug, department, etc.)
   - ☐ bookstore
   - ☐ supermarket
   - ☐ other _____

7. Mind telling your age?
   - ☐ under 18
   - ☐ 18 to 30
   - ☐ 31 to 45
   - ☐ over 45

8. How many SECOND CHANCE AT LOVE novels have you read?
   - ☐ this is the first
   - ☐ some (give number, please _____)

9. How do you rate SECOND CHANCE AT LOVE vs. competing lines?
   - ☐ poor
   - ☐ fair
   - ☐ good
   - ☐ excellent

10. Check here if you would like to
    - ☐ receive the SECOND CHANCE AT LOVE Newsletter

....

Fill-in your name and address below:

name:_____

street address:_____

city_____ state_____ zip_____

Please share your other ideas about romances with us on an additional sheet and attach it securely to this questionnaire.

PLEASE RETURN THIS QUESTIONNAIRE TO:
SECOND CHANCE AT LOVE, THE BERKLEY/JOVE PUBLISHING GROUP
200 Madison Avenue, New York, New York 10016